Pennine Flowers

GLOBEFLOWER

Tyne Gap

CROSS FELL ▲▲ Lt. & Gt. DUN FELLS

Weardale

▲ MELDON HILL

Eden Valley

▲ MICKLE FELL

Teesdale

Swaledale

▲ HIGH SEAT
▲ GREAT
SHUNNER FELL

Wensleydale

Lunesdale

▲WHERNSIDE

INGLEBOROUGH ▲   ▲   ▲ GREAT WHERNSIDE
        PENYGHENT

Nidderdale

Ribblesdale

Wharfedale

Airedale

Calderdale

| 0   10   20   30 miles
| 0 10 20 30 40 kilometres

▲ BLEAKLOW HEAD

KINDER SCOUT▲ ●Edale

Pennine Flowers

by Joan E. Duncan
and R. W. Robson

BOG ASPHODEL

DALESMAN BOOKS

1977

The Dalesman Publishing Company Ltd.,
Clapham (via Lancaster), North Yorkshire
© Joan E. Duncan and R. W. Robson, 1977

ISBN: 0 85206 398 9

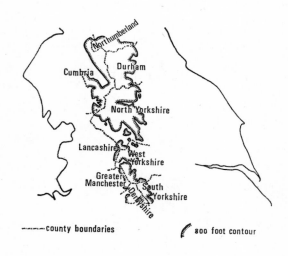

Printed in Great Britain by
Galava Printing Company Ltd., Hallam Road, Nelson, Lancs.

Contents

Illustrations

Cover Photograph: Mountain Pansy, by Freda C. Draper.
Maps and Drawings by Joan E. Duncan.

The photographs: Gordon Wood, 41; Helen Lefèvre, 42, 43; R.
W. Robson, 44; Herman Hemingway, 45; Yorkshire Naturalists'
Trust, 46; C. H. Wood, 47; Clifford Robinson, 48; P. Acomb,
back cover.

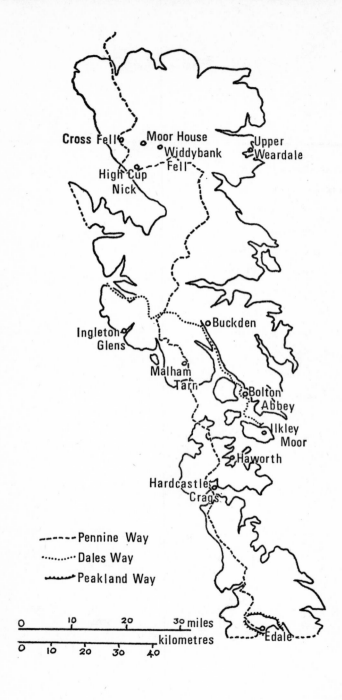

Cross Fell

Moor House
Widdybank
Fell

Upper
Weardale

High Cup
Nick

Buckden

Ingleton
Glens

Malham
Tarn

Bolton
Abbey

Ilkley
Moor

Haworth

Hardcastle
Crags

----- Pennine Way
.... Dales Way
⌇⌇⌇ Peakland Way

Edale

0   10   20   30 miles
0   10   20   30   40 kilometres

An Introduction

THERE is a freshness and at times an undefinable fragrance to the air at high altitude in the Pennines, which in spring can be borne from the blooming of the bluebells or primroses growing in secluded montane woodlands. During summer, the treading on the banks where the wild thyme grows makes an appreciation that is not easy to define (or describe), while later the "bonny purple heather" attracts people as well as bees to the scent and beauty of the hills.

The authors of *Pennine Flowers* would like to encourage others to enjoy the flora of the Pennines as much as they do themselves. As a companion volume to *Pennine Birds*, its aim is to suggest some of the ways in which a study of the flowers may be approached; it is designed to be a general guide to the visitor. For those taking long distance walks, wild flowers may be appreciated simply for their beauty in the countryside, but on shorter walks, and at a slower pace, further pleasure can be gained from finding out the name of a plant, the kind of place or habitat in which it grows, and at what time of the year it may be seen in flower. This could lead to continued study in several directions as, for example, in discovering which plants make up a certain type of vegetation; the family relationships of species, and the folklore.

Unlike birds, plants do not move away and are there for the searching, provided one knows how and where to look. The area under consideration is defined for the purpose of this book as the high ground of the north of England above the 800 foot contour (approx. 250 metres), from North Derbyshire to the Tyne Gap. Also included are the many gills or cloughs cut by the tributaries and higher reaches of the rivers, for these, with the upland country, are a typical feature of the Pennines.

The Plant List

As this book is a guide rather than a definitive work, a complete flora list has not been given; in the main, the species omitted are the very rarest and those recognised as being difficult for the beginner to identify. Apart from this, it is hoped that the plants named will make a useful check list, and for those who like to keep a "tick list" it could be used for this purpose. Reference to the list is recommended during the reading of the preceding chapters. It is based on *English Names of Wild Flowers* (1974).

Numerically, the plant list is much greater than that of birds and may seem formidable to the beginner. It is easier to understand if some simple classification is considered. The groups of plants which are of interest in the context of this guide are all vascular plants—that is, those which have a conducting system for carrying water, nutrients and food, as distinct from the algae, mosses, liverworts, lichens and fungi. Not all the vascular plants bear flowers, although for simplicity this term is used in the title. Some are spore-bearing and include the clubmosses, horsetails and ferns; the conifers produce seeds but not flowers, and the rest are true flowering, seed-producing plants. This is by far the largest group and it must be remembered that a number of these, such as rushes, sedges and grasses, which do not have spectacular flowers are nonetheless flowering plants.

The order of the list follows that in the *Flora of the British Isles*, by Clapham, Tutin and Warburg. This, the scientific order, has the advantage of keeping together the species in the same family. The English and scientific names given are those recommended by the Botanical Society of the British Isles as applicable over Britain in the book *English Names of Wild Flowers*, by Dony, Rob and Perring. Many plants have more than one English name. If a name different from the one in the list is locally used in the Pennines, this is mentioned in the list or text.

Identification

There are several reliable illustrated flower books on the market, and the use of one or more of these is recommended. It is better to consult more than one book for both description and diagrams. A picture or photograph alone should never be relied upon, as this could be misleading, especially with closely related species where the differences in structure may be small but critical and would be best shown by a diagram or detailed description.

Clearly the use of a Flora with a key to names is advisable in these cases, but the beginner with little knowledge of the scientific terms needed here might be deterred, and so lose altogether the enjoyment of flower study. Thus, identification of as many plants as possible from illustrated books would make a good start with the aim of progressing to the use of a flora in the future. Some guidelines are given in the chapter on naming the plant.

Conservation

Nature Conservation must always be uppermost in the mind of any naturalist, not least when looking for flowers either alone or in company with others. Both plants and their habitats must be guarded.

The Conservation of Wild Creatures and Wild Plants Act 1975 makes illegal the uprooting of wild plants, and 21 rare species listed for special protection must not be picked. Although it is not illegal to pick common plants, this is not advised and the botanist should exercise strict self-discipline. A plant should be allowed to flower and produce its full quota of seed, thus completing its life cycle naturally. A flower must often be examined closely through a lens, but this can be done on the spot without picking. We cannot do better than quote the maxim "Take the book to the plant, not the plant to the book", used in the introduction to *The Wild Flowers of Britain and Northern Europe*, by Richard and Alastair Fitter, illustrated by Marjorie Blamey. They give some useful advice to the beginner, including an important reminder that should an unknown and possibly rare plant be found it is better to leave it and take a botanist friend to see it than to present him with a specimen.

The habitats of some plants are very vulnerable and a plant may be seriously threatened by botanists unless the utmost care is taken to avoid disturbance. Trampling impacts the soil, or may expose a sheltered plant, endangering it through the alteration of its immediate environment. The botanist who rightly prefers a colour slide to a pressed specimen may still do harm if, in the attempt to obtain a perfect close-up, he exposes the plant to view and to the elements.

There are certain instances of plants called "critical species" whose identification requires an expert. In such cases information should be sought as to the appropriate referee and the material he would need to examine. Examples of Pennine flowers in this category are hawkweeds, brambles and some of the water plants. However, the student should have acquired considerable expertise in the identification of other plants before this stage is reached.

The essential equipment for the field botanist includes a good hand lens (x 10) and a notebook and pencil, along with the most handy flower book. A complete list of the plants found during an expedition, with the date, is a record worth keeping.

Pennine "Treasures"

Among the special treasures of the Pennines are plants that are rare over the country as a whole but plentiful in certain upland areas of the Pennines. Others may be very specific in their habitat requirements, or be unusual in structure or colour. In any case they merit a chapter of their own. Not all the plants are confined to the Pennines. A good number of common plants will be found which grow in high places as well as elsewhere because they have a wide altitudinal range.

As to how all these plants may be found, the notes are intended as a guide to the type of habitat where they may be expected to grow rather than as an indication of locality. In this way the beginner botanist can learn much more about the species. It is difficult to decide which gives the greater satisfaction—the finding of a plant by recognising the right habitat, or the unexpected discovery of a plant one has never seen before. It is certainly better to be the real finder than simply to be taken to the spot by somebody else.

Nevertheless, botanising with others is more enjoyable than travelling on one's own; it can be profitable, too, for the help and hints on identification that can be exchanged. Many amateur botanists owe much to experts who have helped them in the field. Readers may like to get in touch with other botanists, through one of the local natural history societies based on or near the Pennines. Information can usually be obtained from local libraries and museums. County naturalists' trusts, which administer nature reserves and are concerned with nature conservation over the whole county, need both practical and financial help from those who care about our wildlife.

However interesting flowers may be in their own right, the study of plants is enhanced and better understood if they are considered in relation to their natural habitat. For this reason, the reader should have some background knowledge, however slight, of the history of vegetation in the Pennines, the basic geology and the distribution of vegetation as it is today. The influence of man's activities on the vegetation pattern is of far-reaching importance. These concepts are given in outline in the first chapters, but many books and papers may be consulted. Some of these are included in the bibliography.

Acknowledgements

We are grateful to our many naturalist friends for answering our questions and helping in various ways, especially to:

Dr. M. E. Bradshaw, Miss E. Crackles, Mrs. F. C. Draper, Mr. A. C. M. Duncan, Miss H. Lefèvre, Dr. G. A. Nelson, Mr. J. Parkin, Dr. F. H. Perring, Dr. A. Raistrick, Dr. W. A. Sledge, Mr. G. Wood.

We thank Mr. W. R. Mitchell, of *The Dalesman*, for giving us invaluable advice and co-ordinating our efforts.

A Geological Outline

BEFORE looking at the present flora of the Pennines, it will be of interest to find out something about the geology of the land upon which the flora developed. For this it is necessary to go back in time some 500 million years. Geological evidence reveals a fascinating story of the vast changes which must have taken place on the earth, sometimes violently, and at other times more slowly under calm conditions, but each period taking millions of years.

The following is a brief and somewhat simplified survey of how these changes affected the Pennine area, but we hope it will give a little of the background and stimulate the reader to learn to recognise different regions of the Pennines and then to relate the flora to the geology. For further study of this subject there are many books available, including *The Pennine Dales* in which Dr. Arthur Raistrick gives an interesting and vivid account.

Events causing the changes followed a definite sequence—rock formation under water; mountain building; erosion; then inundation by the sea again. The cycle continued. The rocks of more than 500 million years ago, known as pre-Cambrian, would be formed and altered in this way. In the sea which covered the pre-Cambrian land there began again the deposition of mineral particles that were compressed into sedimentary rock. Throughout some 200 million years, successive layers of rock were laid down and are now known as Cambrian, Ordovician, Silurian and Devonian. Earth movements caused the rocks to be folded upwards, and a land of high mountains emerged from the sea. Due to folding, the rock layers or strata were tilted up, so that when subsequently the mountains were worn down by erosion, the edges of the strata formed the uneven surface.

It was on this surface, when the land became once more submerged under the sea, that the rocks forming the Pennines as we know them today were laid down. The new strata, being horizontal, are lying across the tilted older layers and such a formation is known as an unconformity, examples of which may be seen in several parts of Craven, especially in the Ingleton area. The rocks now forming, about 330 million years ago, were the start of the Carboniferous series and laid down in what must have been a warm tranquil period. Formed from the limy protective cases of countless sea creatures, they were to become the Great Scar limestone of today. Above this were deposited the rocks known as the Yoredale series; they were formed in shallowing seas and consist of successive layers of limestone, sandstone and shales, an indication that silts were being brought down by rivers. Further evidence of this comes from the thin coal seams of this period, the result of the partial decay of the land plants that had evolved to grow on the mudbanks. The sea was receding, and from a continent to the north came rivers with huge deltas where coarser sand and muds were the ingredients of the sandstones and shales of the Millstone Grit. The rivers, flowing from north to south, left a fairly thin layer of this rock in the north and a much thicker layer at the south. The ground now was very wet and in the swampy conditions grew the dense forests of huge trees whose remains gave rise to the coal measures. This is the upper layer of the series named, as a whole, the Carboniferous series, from these "carbon-bearing" rocks.

After the coal measures had been deposited came a period of earth movements resulting in the uplift of the Pennines. As well as being folded, the rocks, subject as they were to great stress, became cracked or faulted vertically and then earth movements caused the land on one side of the fault to be pushed up higher than the other. The Craven fault system is one of the most prominent. The Whin Sill in the north was intruded through cracks as molten rock at this time. Mineral veins were deposited in many of the smaller cracks.

It was a very long time before the sea once more submerged the Pennines and in the interim they existed as an island. The Permian limestone and New Red Sandstone of the Permo-Triassic desert period were formed under the sea but did not reach the height of the Pennines. In the calm Cretaceous period, about 70 to 80 million years ago, the sea again covered the Pennines and deposited a layer of chalk. During the Tertiary period that followed and lasted until about one million years ago, the Pennines were uplifted again and subjected to weathering. The rivers cut their courses through the chalk and continued the same routes through the underlying rock when the chalk layer was worn away.

Towards the end of the Tertiary period the climate was becoming colder and this culminated in the Great Ice Age. The ice had far-reaching effects on the Pennines, clearing the higher ground of weathered rock debris and depositing large quantities in lower areas, often as boulder clay. Glacial moraines blocked valleys and held back the melt water so that glacial lakes formed. The ice smoothed the rocks and deepened valleys. In much of the northern Pennines the layer of Millstone Grit was eroded away in pre-glacial periods, revealing the limestone. The summits of the mountains were not ice-covered and some retain traces of a glacial flora and their capping of Millstone Grit. Parts of the southern Pennines also escaped the ice; the gritstone blocks have not been smoothed by ice, but weathered into strange shapes.

ERA	PERIOD	million years ago (approx.)
Quaternary	RECENT	
Tertiary	PLIOCENE	
	MIOCENE	
	OLIGOCENE	
	EOCENE	65 m
Secondary	CRETACEOUS	
	JURASSIC	
	TRIASSIC	190 m
Primary	PERMIAN	
	CARBONIFEROUS	
	DEVONIAN	
	SILURIAN	
	ORDOVICIAN	
	CAMBRIAN	
		500 m
Pre-Cambrian	PRE-CAMBRIAN	

Geological Column

The Flora in Prehistory

THE present flora of the Pennines has a history dating back to the end of the Ice Age, 10,000 to 11,000 years ago apart from traces of a glacial flora mentioned above. The whole of the Ice Age was not just one continuous period of frost, but warmer periods intervened, long enough for vegetation to become established. However, each time this would be mainly destroyed by the next glaciation, except for a few species sufficiently resistant to frost to survive in isolated pockets or on any high ground not covered by ice. Thus the flora (and fauna) would have to make a fresh start, so to speak, the ground newly exposed as the ice melted being colonised through the northward migration of those species living beyond the ice sheet. This never reached as far south as what is now the south coast of England.

After the last glaciation, Britain was still joined to Europe. Nowhere near enough species of plants came from the south to make the British flora as varied as that of the Continent as a whole before our islands became isolated. The formation of the English Channel about 7,500 years ago is of significance because the sea barrier put an end to most plant migration by natural means into this country. Only those species known to be growing here then are counted as native to Britain.

Much of the evidence that indicates which plants have grown here since the Ice Age comes from plant remains preserved in peat. These range from larger portions such as wood and bark, the leaves of Sphagnum moss with cell structure preserved, seeds, and microscopic remains like spores and pollen grains whose outer coats are very resistant to decay. The Pennine moors, where deposits of peat have accumulated, are rich sources of such evidence. This is acid peat, consisting of incompletely decayed remains of moorland plants. With high rainfall and impeded drainage, the ground becomes waterlogged and therefore short of air, while the acids of decay are not neutralised because there are few mineral salts in rainwater. These anaerobic and highly acid conditions are not the right medium for bacteria of decay to function and peat is an ideal place for the preservation of remnants of plants once growing where peat has formed and the spores and pollen grains blown in from plants round about.

Taking a boring from a bed of peat is like revealing a history book in nature. From it can be read, by microscopical examination and pollen analysis, the story of the succession of plants. Radio-carbon dating can determine the ages of the different layers of peat.

The plant succession gives a clue to the climatic changes which have influenced the vegetation. In the late-glacial and early post-glacial times tundra, as in the Arctic today, was predominant; then, as the climate became warmer in the Boreal period, this was succeeded by forests of birch and pine, with alder in wetter parts. The tree limit was up to 2,000 feet O.D. It was during the Boreal/Arctic transition period of cooler, wetter weather that peat began to form on the Pennine plateaux from plant communities of cotton grass and Sphagnum moss above 1,200 feet. Trees could no longer survive at this altitude and the forests gave way to acid moor. By the time the Atlantic period came, with the climate becoming still wetter, Sphagnum peat became so thick that its surface was above the ground-water level. The only source of water would now be rain, with a few of the mineral salts that are present in ground-water, giving the acid conditions mentioned above. This kind of peat (ombrogenous) exists in two states in the Pennines: raised bogs, which are domed, developed over the beds of glacial lakes, and blanket bog on higher ground where rainfall was very heavy and a great depth of peat covered both flat and sloping ground.

About 2,500 years ago, the cool temperate Atlantic climate as we know it today was established. The natural vegetation of deciduous woodland grew and reached its climax, of mixed oakwoods, birch scrub at higher altitudes and, above the tree line on drier ground, moorland communities such as heather and bilberry.

During post-glacial times the scene was set for the entrance of Man. In his book *Man's Place in Nature*, Teilhard de Chardin described the "uncanny feeling" of a traveller transported to our planet when he could roam the whole earth, a world almost our world, and yet meet literally nobody. Compared with this he pictured the superabundance of man "cluttering the whole prospect ... man inundating like a flood the whole countryside and every remnant of wild fauna."

The Early Stone Age and Middle Stone Age men would hunt for their food in the environment and have little effect on it but, later, Neolithic Man learnt how to use and control natural resources. He began to change his surroundings, clearing forests to make room for cultivation and grazing his stock, thus preventing the natural vegetation from reaching its forest climax. Archaeological evidence must go hand in hand with other evidence to show how the vegetation has changed since man came. It must be remembered, however, that natural changes are going on also, and although many direct results of man's activity are clear to see, the influences of nature play a vital part. The whole picture is very complex, but what is evident is that in the Pennines a high proportion of the scenery could be described as "man-made". Several habitats owe their continued existence to man's management whether intentional, as in maintenance of heather moors, or not, as for example limited grazing of limestone pastures which prevents grass from choking out the flowers.

In nature, the plants and animals are interdependent, living together in communities, related to the habitat. Man's interference with the natural sequence of events by using resources of nature for his own ends and his own survival can have a far reaching effect.

MOUNTAIN AVENS

Field Observations

WHATEVER changes have occurred in our flora, the wild plants growing today are there for our enjoyment. "Live the Botany!" was the instruction given by the enthusiastic Norwegian botanist, Professor Nordhagen, expressing so succinctly the pleasure to be gained from plant study. The best place to begin is with the plants themselves as they grow, so we will away to the Pennines, always remembering that background reading is a useful introduction but will have still more meaning and value after experience in the field.

In the following section, we give examples of Pennine scenery and habitats that illustrate the geology and related vegetation, including some of the features mentioned above. There is no space here to give lists of plant species for each habitat, but most of the area can be covered by consulting *The Natural History of Upper Teesdale*, *The Naturalist's Yorkshire* and *The Peak District*. Details of these are given in the book list along with other useful references.

In the chapter on Flowering Plants and Ferns in *The Naturalist's Yorkshire*, Dr. Sledge introduces his account of the different Yorkshire habitats by explaining that the types of vegetation are determined by the mineral content, moisture content and texture of the soil, "but the factors of overriding importance regarding habitat preferences of species and plant communities," he adds, "are the acidity or alkalinity of the soils to which the underlying rocks give rise, together with drainage conditions." This is a helpful starting point. As has been shown, the peaty areas are certainly acid, and the soils derived from siliceous rocks (grits and shales) are also acid. In limestone areas, the calcareous rocks give rise to an alkaline or basic soil.

Quite different vegetation is supported by these two sharply contrasting types, and they are distinguishable on sight by appearance and the rocks themselves. Comparatively few species will grow on an acid soil and the vegetation is of a rather dull colour, albeit giving attractive colour changes through the seasons. The effect is made darker in the Pennines near industrial areas where

17

the rocks are blackened by smoke pollution. There is little competition between species, some of which spread over large areas, for example, cotton grass in wet areas, heather, bilberry, crowberry, on drier parts, and mat grass on lower slopes. Many more species favour an alkaline soil and the bright green grass and light coloured rocks give a completely different picture from the other.

There are places in the Pennines where this marked contrast may be seen. The walker on the Pennine Way crossing the Aire Gap will note the change from the gritstone moors to the Craven limestone. While walking up Wharfedale, along part of the Dales Way, from Bolton Abbey to Burnsall, one can see the millstone grit give way to limestone, and there are places where the drystone walls are a mixture of gritstone and limestone blocks, the limestone being near the surface of the ground where the other layer is thinning out. The road from Settle up Buckhaw Brow follows the line of the South Craven Fault, and here an abrupt change of vegetation from one side of the road to the other is seen: the upthrow side is limestone from which the cover of gritstone has been eroded, while typical millstone grit vegetation of lower ground is seen on the downthrow side. On a much smaller scale, the nature trail in Upper Teesdale along the Birkdale Track goes through the "patchwork" of vegetation of both types.

The difference in species number was well demonstrated during a botanical excursion not far from one section of the Pennine Way which traverses a tract of peaty moor above limestone country. Groups separated to investigate different limited areas. One party returned with a list of under 100 flowering plants from the fell top, while another, having examined a limestone area of grassland and flushes not a mile away, recorded well over 200 species.

Some species of plants are not demanding of acid or basic conditions and will grow in either, or in neutral soil, but there are certain plants that are strictly confined to one of the first two situations. Those growing only in basic soil are called calcicoles, while those unable to grow here are known as calcifuges. The terms come from the Latin words *calx* = chalk; *colo* = I inhabit, and *fugo* = I flee. Their presence in a particular area can be an indication of the condition they favour.

An apparent misfit in limestone country is heather, seemingly growing on top of the limestone, whereas it would be more at home on an acid moor. The reason here is drainage. Water rapidly drains through limestone, removing bases from the soil and leaving it acid. When this happens a layer of peaty soil develops on the surface and heather can thrive. Similarly tracts of bracken, a species typical of acid soil, are often seen on higher limestone slopes.

18

The older, siliceous, rocks on which the limestone is resting may be exposed below a scar and, since these are much less permeable, alkaline water draining through the limestone will run out over the ground as a limy flush. Such areas are very rewarding to the botanist.

The pattern of acid and basic soils will not always correspond to the geological map, because at lower levels ground may be covered by drift — that is, soil brought by ice or water from another part.

When looking for flowers, therefore, the most important idea to keep in mind is that there are three main types of soil, acid, neutral and alkaline. Small variations give the added interest of possibly finding an unexpected species.

A number of geological features in the Pennines have been mentioned and here are some places where they may be seen. The millstone capping of the high points often gives a distinctive shape, above the more readily weathered limestone below. Wild Boar Fell, Ingleborough and Penyghent are good examples. Weathering of millstone grit which escaped the smoothing action of the ice is seen in the strange shapes of Brimham Rocks, while the gritstone "edges" of the south-west Pennines are prominent features of the scenery there. The stepped horizon often seen in the Pennines is due to the unequal weathering of the sandstone and softer shales where they alternate in layers, the former making steep ridges and the latter gentle slopes.

Weathering of the Yoredales gives a similar effect, with the limestone and sandstone bands forming long ridges separated by shale as in Upper Wensleydale, the valley of the Ure, from which the Yoredale series was named. Owing to the presence of both types of rock here, the flora is rich and varied. The Great Scar Limestone of Craven is very spectacular as, for example, in Ribblesdale and around Malham where the Cove is well known. Under the action of rainwater containing carbon dioxide in solution, limestone is dissolved, and great blocks of the stone have been so weathered into the clints of limestone pavements with deep grikes between. It is here where, sheltered from weather and grazing, a number of shade-loving plants grow.

In the north of the Pennines lies Cross Fell, the highest point of the range. The summit plateau stretches from east to west for over 1,200 yds, and from north to south, from nearly 250 yds to about 800 yds. In similar fashion to the rest of the Northern Pennines, Cross Fell forms part of the anticline; it rises steeply from the Eden Valley, on the west side, but slopes away gradually to the east. It is capped at the summit by millstone grit which is very noticeable to the climber who uses any route other than the recognised paths. The Whin Sill gives an interesting flora and spectacular scenery, as at High Force, Falcon Clints, Cauldron

Snout and High Cup Nick.

Next are some illustrations relating to the section on vegetation history. In Upper Teesdale may be found a flora of great scientific importance, being a "unique assemblage" of plants, relics of the tundra which in early post-glacial times covered the Pennines. In *The Natural History of Upper Teesdale*, the chapters by Dr. Margaret Bradshaw and others on the flora, its origin and history, show how interesting and exciting this area is for the botanist. This is borne out by the numbers of students, young and old, who have repeatedly taken part in Dr. Bradshaw's research field weeks in recent years.

There are many examples of blanket peat in the Pennines. The Kinder Plateau in the south and Fleet Moss, between Wensleydale and Upper Wharfedale, are but two. Degeneration of peat which once was very wet and grew cotton grass occurs when drainage sets in. The peat dries out and erosion round the drainage channels leaves the peat standing out as "hags", on whose drying surface heather will grow. If erosion continues, the peat hags become more reduced until finally the whole peat cover is washed away.

The raised bogs or mosses, formed in hollows, are less likely to share this fate, and cotton grass flourishes. Featherbed Moss, aptly named from the wealth of cotton grass, so conspicuous in fruit, is a classic example and, like the Kinder Plateau, is crossed by the Pennine Way.

To watch peat-boring is an interesting experience. The particular bog chosen was on a moor, and we already had some clues to the make-up of the peat from the banks of a stream which cut through the shallower peat at the edge of the moss. A number of pieces of preserved birch wood were seen in the peat, and below the peat was a layer of fine clay of a dull sandy colour. Out in the centre of the moss the borer was inserted and worked down to successive levels, each time the mechanism being turned to bring up a core at that particular depth. The samples were carefully preserved in labelled containers for future pollen analysis by an expert who found that alder pollen was the most abundant. When, finally, the lowest layers had been reached, the whole depth at the point of boring was found to be 12 feet. From below the peat came up a sample of very fine blue-grey clay. This was part of the same clay layer we had seen in the stream bank, but unaltered by weathering, and it had originally settled in the former glacial lake on whose site the peat had developed. We were handling something which had not seen the light of day for 6,000 to 7,000 years, for such was the estimated age of the peat.

As explained previously, the upper tree limit was at a higher altitude in Boreal times than today, but relics of the ground flora of those woods may still be found on high ground, where woodland species such as wood anemone, wood sorrel and blue-bell persist in sheltered places. The deep valleys and cloughs of the Pennines harbour mixed deciduous woodland of oak and other species, a very good example on the millstone grit being Hardcastle Crags. In limestone districts, a mixed woodland dominated by ash is typical and this has a very rich and varied ground flora.

Much more could be said about the Pennine flora in general, but from now on, according to the title of the book, we shall concern ourselves with the flowers themselves.

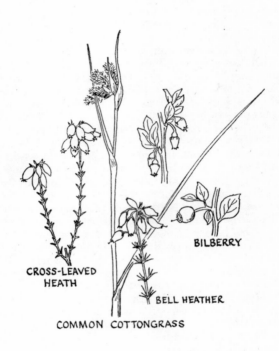

CROSS-LEAVED
HEATH

BILBERRY

BELL HEATHER

COMMON COTTONGRASS

Hints on Identification

THE observations in the previous chapter could be made at any time of the year and many plants identified, but it is in the flowering season that they give most enjoyment of detail. In the interests of conservation, it has already been stated that picking wild flowers should be avoided and that the botanist out-of-doors should take a flower book and hand lens for use in identifying plants. There are advantages in this method because the whole plant can be studied as it appears in its own habitat. It is important to notice the general habit of the plant, for instance whether it creeps or is tufted. The leaves may vary in shape in different parts of the plant and the effect of colour, texture and hairiness or otherwise are best seen when the plant is growing. Finally, the inflorescences present may show all stages of flower buds, flowers and fruits. Examination through a hand lens is often necessary and this, too, can be done on the spot.

However, it would not be helpful to start flower study in this way without some practice and familiarity with flowers beforehand. There are plenty of weeds in gardens or waste places which may be picked with impunity for detailed investigation with flower books available and the necessary adjuncts of hand lens, notebook and pencil. Ideally, reference should also be made to a Flora, but for the beginner this may be somewhat daunting owing to the number of botanical terms used, and the need to keep consulting the glossary. So work with a Flora could be deferred until a later stage. While realising the need for these terms to give full and accurate botanical descriptions, in this book we try to keep the use of them to a minimum.

Within this basic structure there are many variations and it will soon be noticed how flowers in the same family have their own particular shape, often quite distinctive.

A good beginning would be to look for the three common species of buttercup: meadow (*Ranunculus acris*), creeping (*R. repens*) and bulbous (*R. bulbosus*), because they illustrate several important points in connection with identifying and recognising plants. They are obviously closely related from the appearance of the flowers, but there are significant differences: meadow buttercup has a thin unfurrowed flower stalk and the sepals remain upright or erect; the other two have furrowed flower stalks, but in creeping buttercup the sepals are erect, while those of bulbous buttercup turn back and become reflexed. Once this has been discovered, it becomes easy to recognise each species and so proceed to noticing the subtler differences in the three flowers. Then the appearance of each whole plant will be seen to be distinctive and details here can be checked with the flower book. Soon, through constant observation the species can be recognised whether in flower or not. At the same time, habitat preferences will be evident.

Exercises of this type are therefore a good preparation for fieldwork, but we are anxious to be off exploring the Pennines again. There will be time between visits to improve efficiency.

Two quite different habitats have been chosen. In each a number of plants are found which may be puzzling. Although much could be written about their adaptations to the habitat, this section is concerned mainly with their identification by giving hints to assist in the use of a flower book.

Acid Moorland

Not all the plants would necessarily be found in the same moorland area, but this is the kind of place where they grow.

Seven members of the heather family (*Ericaceae*) will be discussed first. The three heathers make a fairly easy start, the "bonny purple heather" or ling (*Calluna vulgaris*) being well-known. The sheen on each little flower must surely be the cause of the beautiful glow from patches of heather at the height of the flowering season. Bell heather (*Erica cinerea*), a plant of sandy areas, has a bell-like magenta flower and narrow dark green leaves, and cross-leaved heath, (*E. tetralix*) has paler pink flowers and, as its name implies, leaves arising in fours in the shape of a cross. It is a greyish looking plant growing in wet places.

Several of the moorland plants called ". . . berry" may be confusing to the beginner. Bilberry, also known as blaeberry or whortleberry (*Vaccinium myrtillus*) has pink, almost globular flowers and a dark purple fruit with a bloom and staining juice. The small broadly oval leaves are thin and are shed in winter, leaving the green winged stems to carry on photosynthesis in compensation.

The next two are evergreens with brown woody stems. Cowberry or red whortleberry (*Vaccinium vitis-idaea*), with pinkish flowers and red fruits, has leaves of similar shape to bilberry leaves, but thicker, darker and glossy; the pale undersides are dotted with small round glands (I first learnt to remember this plant by saying "spotted cow"). Bearberry (*Arctostaphylos uva-*

ursi) is rare in the Pennines, found at high altitudes; it has similar coloured flowers and fruits to cowberry, but its leaves are distinguishable by the well-marked network of veins.

Cranberry is a plant to be sought in sphagnum bogs over which it creeps by very thin stems bearing small dark green leaves. The pretty little pink blooms have petals turned back in the manner of a cyclamen flower and the red fruits, of cranberry sauce fame, appear quite large for so dainty a plant.

Crowberry is placed in a related family of its own (*Empetraceae*). When this dark coloured evergreen plant is growing vigorously, it forms dense mats on the ground and sometimes festoons over rocks. The species commonly found in the Pennines (*Empetrum nigrum*) has separate male and female plants. It flowers at the beginning of spring, which is very early for an upland plant, and is a wind-pollinated plant. Walking over a male colony will shake off the fine, dry pollen which forms clouds. The crimson flowers of both sexes are well worth finding to observe through a lens. The fruit is black and not particularly palatable.

Two common plants of the rough grassland may be noted for comparison with related species later. Tormentil (*Potentilla erecta*), a four-petalled yellow flower, and heath bedstraw (*Galium saxatile*) whose flowers have four small white petals.

Marsh pennywort (*Hydrocotyle vulgaris*) is a common plant of sphagnum bogs. The round leaves with stalks at their centres are easy to see, but a search must be made for the inconspicuous small flowers on the creeping stems which are often hidden among the moss. An attractive creeping plant sometimes found in similar situations is bog pimpernel (*Anagallis tenella*), which has small rounded leaves and striking delicate pink flowers. One of the smallest orchids may occasionally be discovered among sphagnum. This is the lesser twayblade (*Listera cordata*), often little more than $2\frac{1}{2}$ ins. tall with a single pair of leaves and a spike of tiny orchid-shaped flowers. This charming little plant is easily overlooked, but the beginner with a keen eye might just come across it and have one of those unforgettable experiences which give a special dimension to flower study.

Three species of rush make an interesting study. They are all of the type which does not have normal leaves. Brownish flowers grow in a cluster from the side of a stem with a long pointed tip. Soft rush (*Juncus effusus*) has the thickest stems of the three, smooth and yellow-green; next is compact rush (*J. subuliflorus*, previously named *J. conglomeratus*) with a ridged stem, especially noticeable just below the inflorescence, and lastly hard rush (*J. inflexus*) has thin, blue-green rather glaucous stems. The clusters of flowers are longer stalked and spreading in soft and hard rush, but in a tight bunch in compact rush. One pitfall to avoid is that of confusing the compact form of soft rush with the true compact rush. Rushes are found in quantity where they grow, so some may be picked for examination of the pith. This is continuous in the first two species, which in olden times were used for rush lights. The interrupted or ladder-like pith of hard rush would be no use for this purpose.

Other rushes may be found with narrow green leaves and the inflorescence of brown flowers at the top of a stalk. As an example, heath rush (*J. squarrosus*) may be taken, for this is distinguishable, whether flowering or not, by stiff leaves that bend outwards at the base to give the plant a funnel-shape. It may grow in sphagnum or can hold its own among close-growing moorland grasses. The habit corresponds to the growth of rosette plants in lawns.

Ferns, sedges and grasses will also be noted in this habitat, but they are included in another chapter.

Before proceeding to the second habitat, it would be well to consider how a botanical excursion is to be recorded. During the outing a list of species should be made and it is a matter of personal preference how this is done. A standard list could be taken and the species ticked off as found, or a list written down in the order of finding. The latter has the advantage of being a reminder of the route, and habitat notes can be added. Later, the records could be transferred to a notebook, diary or index cards. A pictorial record of sketches or photographs would make a useful addition.

If all this seems too ambitious for the beginner who simply wants to identify and enjoy the flowers, the date and place where found could be written beside the name in the flower book most used, or the list in this book would serve and also challenge the reader to find any additional species not included.

Limestone Grassland

Several of the most attractive and colourful species of the limestone flora which are easy to identify are included in another chapter. These are not the only species on the limestone fells, and looking around in late May and June, one is impressed by the large number of little white flowers. Some of these, and a few larger ones, form the subject of this section. Closer observation reveals that although they can all be described as white, there is a surprising variety in the shade, quality and texture of the petals of different species.

Heath bedstraw has already been mentioned. As it has a wide range of altitude, and can grow on acid or basic soil, it may be found here. On the higher limestone grassland is a much rarer species, the limestone bedstraw (*Galium sterneri*). It has creamier flowers than the pure white of the common species, but they may be distinguished by looking through a lens at the tiny prickles on the leaf margins. Those of heath bedstraw point forwards and those of the limestone species backwards.

Fairy flax (*Linum catharticum*), also known as cathartic flax from its purgative properties, is a common plant of limestone grassland but can also grow elsewhere. It is a delicate little plant whose white flowers hang on very slender stalks.

Eyebrights certainly live up to their name as they sparkle in the grass although this is not the only reason for the name. The corolla has dark lines and is often tinged with violet. Owing to the large number of species and hybrids in the genus to which eyebrights belong, and the difficulties in identification, determination should be checked with an expert. So for the present it may be recorded as *Euphrasia officinalis,* sometimes referred to as *Euphrasia* agg. which is a so-called aggregate name to include all the British species except an Irish one, *E. salisburgensis.*

The three white saxifrages go up in large steps of flower size. Rue-leaved saxifrage (*Saxifrage tridactylites*), "three-fingered leaves", mossy saxifrage (*S. hypnoides*) or Dovedale moss, and meadow saxifrage (*S. granulata*), with large white flowers and kidney-shaped leaves, occur more commonly among long grass than in short turf.

Experience with weeds will help for the next species, common mouse-ear (*Cerastium holosteoides*), whose white petals are bifid (partly split) giving the effect of ten instead of five. It has a very wide range of altitude and soil preference and extends to the tops of the Pennines.

Of the same family (*Caryophyllaceae*) are the pearlworts, for example, procumbent pearlwort (*Sagina procumbens*), which is also a common weed. In the wetter areas grows knotted pearlwort (*S. nodosa*), and at first sight it could be confused with spring sandwort, but the distinguishing features of the flowers are: five styles and yellow anthers in knotted pearlwort, and three styles and pink or red anthers in the other. The flower stalks differ, too, knotted pearlwort having small clusters of leaves within the pairs up the stem, giving the reason for its name; it has a knotted feel and appearance.

The familiar daisy (*Bellis perennis*) must not be omitted from this section if only to represent its family (*Compositae*). It is common and widespread, yet surprisingly, when a list of plants seen on a walk is made in order of finding, it may be some time before daisy appears. Perhaps because it is a species so closely associated with man, one thinks of it as more common than is really the case.

This section concludes with four white-flowered species of the wallflower family (*Cruciferae*). The garden wallflower is a good species to examine in detail first to get to know the typical flower

26

structure of the family, so that one can recognise even the smallest flowered members as belonging to it.

Hairy rock-cress (*Arabis hirsuta*) is a dark green hairy plant of limestone rocks with a basal rosette of leaves and numerous stem leaves. The fruits are long, being the shape of wallflower fruits, but they grow stiffly erect close to the stem.

Three whitlow-grasses are small plants which may be found on limestone; all have flowering shoots arising from a basal rosette of leaves. The spring whitlow-grass (*Erophila verna*) is the commonest, differing from the others in having deeply bifid petals and no stem leaves; the oval fruits are flat. Hoary whitlow-grass (*Draba incana*) really does look hoary, especially in its young stage. The petals are slightly notched and the fruits are similar to those of the spring species but twisted. Wall whitlow-grass (*Draba muralis*) is rare on limestone rocks and walls, the petals are not notched, and helpful features to look for are the stem leaves which are broad and toothed.

Some Distinctive Plants

JUNIPER (*Juniperus communis*)

JUNIPER is considered mainly as a limestone plant but belies this statement on the Pennines, where it is scarce; it is plentiful in the Lake District. Juniper "berries" were used as a prime ingredient in Geneva or Hollands Gin, to which they gave flavour and diuretic properties. (Berries used today come mainly from plants cultivated in Hungary.) Juniper berries take two or three years to ripen, so that blue and green berries are found on the same plant. Only the ripe berries are used to make the Oil of Juniper. Although the fruit has a taste that is unwholesome to humans it is readily eaten by sheep.

Juniper was undoubtedly more common at one time on the Pennines as a pinewood relict. Sheep grazing and charcoal-burning have been responsible for its reduction, but it is still well represented in Upper Teesdale. Juniper is well able to resist wind and so it grows well at exposed sites. A study into the decadence of the plant on the Yorkshire Pennines was carried out by the YNU but no significant cause was found (according to *Wild Flowers of the Chalk and Limestone* by J. E. Lousley). Thickets of juniper (and single plants) are known locally as savins. A drug distilled from this plant was used against dropsy.

GLOBEFLOWER (*Trollius europaea*)

Globeflower is a plant typical of rich alpine meadows, where its tall stature and large globe-like yellow flowers make a striking addition to other colourful meadow flowers. It grows well on Pennine upland meadows which are wet enough and may also be found in scrub, copses and open woodland, always confined to the carboniferous limestone.

The Teesdale local name for this flower is Double Dumplings. Its affinity with buttercups is shown by the floral structure, and by two other local names: May Buttercup in Lancashire and Butter Boxes. The third name is given in Lees *Flora of West Yorkshire*, and he suggests that this countrychildren's name, once used in Ribblesdale, Garsdale and Dentdale, comes from the idea of the petals curling over to enclose the butter-coloured stamens like the lid of a box.

SCURVYGRASS (*Cochlearia spp.*)

Scurvygrass is sometimes known as spoonwort. Formerly the fresh herb was taken by sailors as a preventative against scurvy. Its essential oil is of benefit to paralytic and rheumatic cases; a popular tonic drink was once made from it. These references are most probably to the common form, *Cochlearia officinalis*, which is only given the range of 10—15 feet O.D. (Wilson's *Flora of Westmorland*). *C. alpina* is now agreed to be the species found at altitude in the Pennines and spreading down the streams. McClintock and Fitter state: "All scurvy grasses can be variable and perplexing, appearing to merge with each other and to produce innumerable hybrids." It was first found on the Pennines in Derbyshire by John Ray, 1658.

Scurvygrass is a pleasing plant; it forms a close-knit mat on smooth grassy turf.

MOUNTAIN PANSY (*Viola lutea*)

One of the most delightful flowers of the rough limestone grassland is the mountain pansy, whose scientific name indicates its yellow colour. There are, however, several colour forms. The pure yellow flowers, commonest in Derbyshire and Craven, are not uniformly coloured but have paler upper petals. Two other variants are the patterned violet and yellow ones and the all-violet form. The latter is predominant in Teesdale; there is a variety of colour in a single flower with its yellow "eye", violet lower petals and two rich velvety crimson-purple upper petals.

The rarest colour form is a brown shade reported from one of the northern Yorkshire Dales.

Although mountain pansies grow in limestone districts they are not strictly calcicoles. In Derbyshire, they have been found on the brows of limestone dales but also in non-calcareous pastures, though where the soil is only slightly acid. On limestone pastures in Craven, plants are often found in patches on the sides of small hollows. A study of the habitat by Miss O. E. Balme (1954) showed that the plant is limited to particular soil conditions, where free calcium carbonate has been leached from the surface layers; it is unable to take in sufficient potash and phosphate for healthy growth in the presence of free calcium carbonate. Mountain pansy is therefore an indicator plant of an area where leaching is beginning. For this reason it has a patchy local distribution.

COMMON ROCK ROSE (*Helianthemum chamaecistis*)

This plant has a thick woody rootstock. The petal colour can vary from bright yellow—with at times small orange spots at the base of the petals—to rare white and even copper-coloured forms. Rock rose is found over most of Britain but in general it favours the limestone. It is often introduced to gardens to fill out rockeries.

Common rock rose can be met with on Mickle Fell at 2,400 feet, but it is also common at sea level sites. Areas where it used to be found have reverted to acid-bog and it no longer remains. The plant apparently does best where trampling or disturbance of thin limestone soil deters other competitors. One such place is the Fox Tower near Brough where, in the period before the Army took over land for artillery training, and public access was more frequent, the area around could be quite yellow with the prolific blooming. It is no longer to be seen in such quantity but has increased at some places where forest clearance has taken place. The flower will not stand picking; the petals fall directly. Its roots go down to a considerable depth.

SPRING SANDWORT (*Minuartia verna*)

In late spring/early summer, the spoil heaps of old lead mines come to life with a sparkling covering of starry white flowers. These are of spring sandwort, otherwise known as leadwort from its tolerance of this habitat. Even in places where lead has not been mined, the plant may grow and be an indicator of the presence of lead ore in the ground. Ray recorded its locality in 1688 as being "in Derbyshire on the barren earth they dig out of the shafts of the lead mines near Wirksworth."

The whole plant may be suffused with pink, while other populations may have pure white flowers and green stems and leaves. In one area patches of the two colour forms were inter-mingled. The rarer alpine penny-cress (*Thlaspi alpestre*) is some-times associated with leadwort.

WOOD CRANE'S-BILL (*Geranium sanguineum*)

Wood crane's-bill was given the name Thunder Flower, which is used more popularly in Cumbria for the wood anemone. The crane's-bill's Pennine range is from 150 feet—2,100 feet but it is recorded at 3,300 feet in Scotland. Mountain cliffs are a popular site.

The first local record is by Ray (1661) who wrote: "Near Shap in plenty." Wilson, in his *Flora*, stated: "It imparts a beautiful tint to many fields in June, and probably nowhere in England is it more plentiful." A similar effect has been seen in Teesdale. The colour of the wood crane's-bill can be variable, from mauve to a very dark purple, but it never attains the glorious deep blue of the meadow crane's-bill.

Hodgson, in his *Flora of Cumbria* (1898), gives it as common in meadows towards the mountains, but quite uncommon in the great plain of Cumberland, yet he said that it was very abundant at Gamlesby and Gilsland along the East Fellside of the Pennines. At many high-level sites its place is taken by the bloody crane's-bill.

SHINING CRANE'S-BILL (*Geranium lucidum*)

This has small, rounded, shining leaves which at times attain a rich red colour. The pink flowers are similar in shape to those of herb robert. Shining crane's-bill prefers light soils and grikes in limestone pavements as well as in moss and debris on walls. It has been recorded as growing to 1,850 feet on Dent Crag. C.T. & W. mention it as growing up to 2,500 ft., but in general the distribution is scattered. It has been found at low-level sites in the Eden Valley, and near Warcop was at 450 ft. Within two miles, this crane's-bill was seen at 1,200 ft. on limestone cliffs.

WOOD-SORREL (*Oxalis acetosella*)

An early flowering plant, wood-sorrel can be found blooming in April but it usually appears later at high altitudes. It is often found growing in shelter among the cliffs, where it was used as a decorative embellishment to the nest of the ring ouzel. Wood-sorrel is said to be a relict of the days when the Pennines were covered with natural woodland. It ascends to 2,450 ft. on Little Fell.

Some of the attractive white flowers never open and are self-pollinating. It shuns sunshine and so must be searched for in woodland as well as at the cliff sites mentioned. Beech and sessile oak are favoured by the plant because both give much shade. It is peculiar to see the leaves folded in half along their centre rib and all three leaflets placed neatly "side by side to sleep", which is a security against storm, when they also droop their blossom and fold their leaves. The leaves have a pleasantly acid taste and were eaten in spring salads and a type of sauce. Several other pleasing decoctions are quoted as being made from it; it also had medical usage.

Many beechwoods are carpeted with wood-sorrel, and male fern is associated with it. In its cliff sites it can be found in association with greater wood-rush, red campion and rose bay willowherb.

HORSESHOE VETCH (*Hippocrepis comosa*)

This plant has the typical pea-shaped flowers of its family, in a clear yellow, with faint brown lines. It is dependent on chalk or limestone, and on the Pennines found mainly on limestone outcrops or ledges, where it forms an attractive mat of leaves with the heads of flowers extended. As the pods develop, the reason for its scientific name, *Hippocrepis*—literally horseshoe—becomes evident: only alternate ovules ripen into seeds, so that the pod appears to have bulging segments. Each of these becomes crescent or horseshoe-shaped when the pod is brown and ripe.

CLOUDBERRY (*Rubus chamaemorus*)

Cloudberry, or knotberry, is a shy flowering plant of the bramble family which seems to fruit most freely at 1,800—2,500 feet. The single flower is larger than that of the bramble. The mulberry-like leaves of cloudberry are easily distinguished where they occur on peat and often among heather. The fruit is like a large, hard raspberry which turns yellow when ripe.

Thomas Penny collected this plant in northern England in the middle of the 16th century. Its flowering is extremely unpredictable but 1974 was apparently a good year for fruiting; James Parkin, warden of the Moor House Reserve, near Cross Fell, found that it flowered and fruited well in that area.

Max Walters in *Mountain Flowers*, Raven and Walters (1956) suggests that the sterility of large patches is in part due to the greater frequency of the male plant. Quite large patches are occupied by only a single sex, indicating that a vegetative spread by means of the slender rhizomes is of great importance. Although common on the Pennines, it is a rare plant in Lakeland.

STONE BRAMBLE (*Rubus saxatilis*)

Red for the fruit, and "of the stone" for its habitat, is the meaning of the scientific name. The stone bramble, seldom up to one foot high, has spineless thin flowering stems which are annual and grow long, rather glaucous stolons. It is found in limestone

31

woods, where it is easily recognised by its yellow-green leaves with three leaflets. The flowers are inconspicuous with narrow white petals and the fruits a translucent scarlet, like blackberries but with only a few larger sections; they are rather sour to eat.

CINQUEFOILS (*Potentilla spp.*)

If the reader has become familiar with the common species of Potentilla, such as silverweed, creeping cinquefoil and tormentil, and the various cultivated forms of shrubby cinquefoil, then it will be of interest to find three rarer species growing wild. They are all of significance in the history of vegetation, evidence having shown that they grew in southern England 10,000 to 15,000 years ago.

SHRUBBY CINQUEFOIL (*P. fruticosa*)

This is a notable yellow-flowered shrub of Upper Teesdale where it grows by the river on shingle and gravelly banks.

SPRING CINQUEFOIL (*P. tabernaemontani*)

ALPINE CINQUEFOIL (*P. alpina*)

Both grow on carboniferous limestone. The former is more widespread in the Pennines, while the other is very local. Spring cinquefoil is a mat-forming plant often found at the foot of a limestone outcrop and spreading into grassland; its flowers which bloom well from April to June are a palish yellow.

Alpine cinquefoil, on the other hand, is not mat-forming and more likely to be found on dry rock ledges, although it occasionally grows in grassland. The flowers, out in June to July, are a deeper yellow than those of the spring species, often with an orange spot at the base of each petal and are on long upward-curving stalks.

It will be seen that the habitats and flowering periods of the two species could overlap. There are places where they occur near each other, providing a good opportunity for anyone finding them together to compare them.

MOUNTAIN AVENS (*Dryas octopetala*)

Mountain avens is a woody, evergreen, mat-forming plant as distinctive as its scientific name; the beautiful white flowers have eight petals. Dryas could come from dryad, a wood nymph, but it is more likely derived from the Greek word *drus,* originally meaning tree, though it came to be applied to oak, because the glossy dark green wavy-edged leaves are shaped like miniature oak leaves. Closer inspection of the plant shows the pale woolly underside of the leaves and the black glandular hairs on the upper flower stalk and calyx. The flowers have numerous orange stamens. In fruit, the plant is attractive, having heads of feathery fruits.

32

Dryas has an arctic-alpine distribution, as well as growing on mountains. It occurs at sea level as, for example on the Burren in Ireland. Unimpeded by other plants it will spread to form a dense Dryas heath, as is seen on mountain slopes in Norway, and this would most likely be its British status in the late glacial flora.

On the Pennines it was much reduced by the growth of scrub or birch woodland and it now survives on the limestone as a relict species in a few refuges where trees would not grow. Although it thrives well on limstone outcrops, there are places where it is found in patches among rough limestone grassland, having presumably spread from seedlings becoming established in a pocket of bare soil.

BURNET ROSE (*Rosa pimpinellifolia*)

Burnet rose, like the last species, grows both on limestone uplands and by the sea, but it is very much more plentiful. It can spread by suckers and may form dwarf scrub or be a stabiliser of calcareous sand dunes. Growing among limestone outcrops and pavements, it is more likely to exist as separate spreading bushes.

Roses frequently hybridise, and the burnet rose is no exception, but the pure species is not difficult to identify by its very prickly nature (hence the old name, *R. spinosissima*), having many thin straight prickles of different lengths interspersed with stiff bristles, on the stem. The reason for the present name is the resemblance of the pinnate leaves, with up to eleven small leaflets, to those of burnet saxifrage (*Pimpinella saxifraga*). Great burnet and salad burnet have similar leaves too. The burnet rose flowers are white and scented and the small blackish hips are almost globular in shape.

ROSEROOT (*Sedum rosea*)

Roseroot, or Midsummer Men, was recorded by John Ray in 1671 "In excelsis montibus ... Westmorlandiae." Signs of its leaves appear early and it quickly matures to come into flower during May and June. Many of its situations on rock ledges appear to be precarious, but when examined the plant is very secure. Roseroot often makes a colourful picture on what without it would look to be a very bare ledge. The fleshy leaves of this sedum, along with dense heads of greenish-yellow flowers, appear to attract a host of small flies and other insects.

HAIRY STONECROP (*Sedum villosum*)

The stonecrops, "sitting on a stone", have a Latin derivation for their scientific name—*sedeo*=I sit—and an Anglo-Saxon origin for their common name *cropp* meaning a bunch. They have smooth fleshy leaves, thus being well fitted for growth in dry stony places, but unlike other species, hairy stonecrop grows in wet places and has glandular-pubescent leaves, the fine hairs and glands showing up well through a lens. The whole plant is pinkish and, with a mass of pink starry flowers, makes a fine picture in upland limestone districts on flushes, wet stony ground, by springs and along stream sides. Beautiful as it is for man's visual enjoyment, it is also said to be a great delicacy for sheep!

PURPLE SAXIFRAGE (*Saxifraga oppositifolia*)

Purple or mountain saxifrage is an arctic-alpine plant which once grew plentifully in Britain and now has a scattered distribution. On the Pennines, it survives as a relict species on limestone cliffs. The rose-purple flowers come out in early spring when the plant, growing in festoons out of the rock crevices, is at its best. The leaves grow closer together on the non-flowering shoots than on those bearing flowers. Each leaf is small and thickened at the tip with a tiny pit where lime is secreted, causing them to be lime-encrusted, as is the case with some garden saxifrages.

GRASS-OF-PARNASSUS (*Parnassia palustris*)

This is closely related to the saxifrages, which it resembles. It is late to flower. Some Floras give the flowering period from July (even June) to September, but it rarely comes into flower in the Eden Valley before August. This plant is to be found in most marshy high-level situations, even up to 1,800 feet on the Pennines. Its range takes it from the dune-slacks on the coast up to 2,630 ft. on Snowdon.

In *The Handbook of Flower Pollination,* Knuth says that the stalked glands of the staminodes attract insects by their glistening appearance, suggesting abundant nectar. The more intelligent insects do not allow themselves to be deceived by this, but others (flies and beetles) are repeatedly attracted and effect pollination as they seek for the scanty nectar secreted at the base of the staminodes.

ROUND-LEAVED SUNDEW (*Drosera rotundifolia*)

Sundew or dewplant grows up to 1,700 feet in Yorkshire and possibly higher on some Northern Pennine sites. It is found most frequently growing among sphagnum moss and on peaty ground. Its rosette of rounded leaves, covered by hairs which are red-coloured, are tipped with a sticky fluid which traps insects, mainly small flies.

Sundew is our best example of a fly-catching plant. Juices secreted by the leaves can speedily digest the flies. The flowers of the plant are small and white, growing on two or three slender stems which are two to six inches high. In their early stages they are coiled inwards. The flowers open only in really sunny periods; it is apparent that many plants never yield flowers.

Two "newcomers" to the Pennines are included in this selected list because they serve to illustrate how an alien plant, having been brought to this country for cultivation can escape into the wild and, given the right conditions, become established and extend its range. They may both be found in the Pennines.

NEW ZEALAND WILLOWHERB *(Epilobium nerterioides)*

The mat-forming creeping habit of this species makes it unlike other willowherbs in Britain. At first sight, and when not in flower, it could be mistaken for bog pimpernel, since it can grow in similar situations. However, the white flowers and later the fruits are so typical of the willowherbs that there need be no doubt of its identity; also the coppery colouring on the plant is not found on bog pimpernel. The scientific name *nerterioides* comes from its likeness in vegetative habitat to a small creeping plant in New Zealand, a species of *Nertera*.

Epilobium nerterioides was introduced into England as a rock plant. The first escape was noted in 1908. Over the next 25 years there were records from scattered places; it spread quickly in the early thirties and now it frequents the upland streams on the Northern Pennines, both in limestone and in gritstone areas. It was rare in Derbyshire but is now increasing there, too. The plant may also be a weed of waste places and in gardens, and it has been found to flourish in a wet lawn. Nevertheless its original habitat is on stony streamsides and it was of great interest to one of the authors, having often recorded it in the Pennines, to see the New Zealand willowherb at home on the slopes of Mount Egmont.

The following features of the plant appear to contribute to its establishment in this country—ability to root from the stems and to spread over wet stony places where there is little competition from other plants; high seed production after self-fertilisation, therefore not depending on pollen from another plant, and the feathery wind-dispersed seeds, a high proportion of which germinate.

SLENDER SPEEDWELL *(Veronica filiformis)*

This creeping plant is recognised by its typically speedwell-structured flowers on long thread-like stalks, and kidney shaped leaves. Here is a plant that is native to the Caucasian mountains and Asia Minor but has become widely naturalised in Europe. Its introduction into gardens in England was believed to be in

1808, but it was first known to be cultivated in rock gardens in about 1920, being a popular plant until it was found how well it could spread. In the garden it rapidly invades lawns and flower-beds. Having escaped, it has grown well among grass, especially in damp areas near streams.

Unlike New Zealand willowherb, slender speedwell is self-sterile. Even in its native habitat it does not commonly set seed, and fruits are said to be very rare in Britain. Yet it readily roots from the creeping stems, and the smallest piece can be the start of a new colony. This is an example of high success through vegetative reproduction and, since no cross-fertilisation is involved, it is not surprising that most of the plants in this country appear to be of the same strain.

ALPINE BISTORT (*Polygonum viviparum*)

This is an arctic-alpine plant of limestone areas. On short mountain turf it may be only an inch or two high, but it will grow taller among more lush grass. Its old scientific name, *Bistorta minor,* suggests that it is a small version of bistort and, indeed, the leaves are like bistort leaves in miniature although as befits a plant of exposed high places they are fairly thick and slightly inrolled to reduce water loss.

In the flowering spike there is another significant feature also associated with habitat: the upper flowers are normal, but the lower ones are replaced by purplish thickened buds, or bulbils, which drop off and over-winter ready to grow next season. Had the bulbils sprouted while still on the plant, and then fallen to the ground, the method would have been true vivipary, which is found in several mountain plants as a way of reproduction alternative to the somewhat chancy nature of pollination and seed production at high altitude.

The next two species are examples of plants which are very common by the sea but persist as remnants of the late glacial flora in mountainous areas.

THRIFT or SEA PINK (*Armeria maritima*)

Thrift with its familiar heads of pink papery flowers is a compactly tufted plant with strap-like leaves. It may in some parts be found around the lead mine spoil heaps.

SEA PLANTAIN (*Plantago maritima*)

This has similar leaves but the plant is less tufted and more of a rosette type. The little flowers have yellow anthers and grow on a spike which is like that of the broad-leaved plantain on a small scale.

BIRDS-EYE PRIMROSE (*Primula farinosa*)

This is one of the loveliest of the British flowering plants.

It can be found growing in Teesdale at up to nearly 1,800 feet. It has an umbel of up to a dozen lovely lilac-pink flowers growing up to 10 or 12 inches long on a slender stem which is mealy towards the top. The rosette of the basal leaves can also be covered with a white or greenish-white meal. The flowering period is May to June or July. Areas where it grows in limestone country can at times be transformed to most delightful showy places when the plants are blooming at their best.

GENTIANS

The name gentian is said to have come from Gentius, ancient king of Illyria who discovered the medicinal properties of these plants.

SPRING GENTIAN (*Gentiana verna*)

This alpine plant, locally abundant in Upper Teesdale, is a real favourite on account of its deep intense blue; it has, indeed, become an emblem for that area. The flowers, large for the size of the plant, arise singly from rosettes of light green leaves, making a fine show on short limestone turf.

Two plants of the same family, though less spectacular, are good to find in Pennine pastures. FIELD GENTIAN (*Gentianella campestris*) and FELWORT (*G. amarella*) may be distinguished partly by their flower colour, the first having lilac flowers and the second dull purple, and also by the later flowering period of felwort. But a close look at the calyx gives more certain identification: field gentian has two of the four sepals larger and overlapping the others, while in felwort the sepals, numbering either four or five, are equal in size.

The habitats give another guide, for field gentian grows usually on acid or neutral soils and felwort in more basic localities.

BOGBEAN or BUCKBEAN (*Menyanthes trifoliata*)

Bogbean ascends to 3,000 feet in parts of Britain and is recorded at 2,200 ft. on Little Fell. This attractive plant at times covers areas of aquatic marshland with a pinky-white sheen. The pink is most pronounced in the buds that appear at the top of the flower-spike, but the open flower has an attractive fluffy white appearance. The leaves are shiny and trifolate. One of the old-time writers described it as "a bunch of feather-like floures of a white colour, dasht over slightly with a wash of light carnation." This could well fit the description made by a Pennine connoisseur.

COMMON BUTTERWORT (*Pinguicula vulgaris*)

This plant, also known as bog or marsh violet, has leaves forming a rosette and clothed with sticky glands which catch insects. The leaves, which are inclined to roll inwards to assist the plant in obtaining sustenance from insects, are shiny yellow-green and take on the shape of a starfish. A few flowers come up from the rosette on slender stems two to four inches long; they can be seen in flower from May to July. The flower is deep violet in colour with a longer spur. It is frequently found growing on wet rocks and also among sphagnum moss and along the banks of streams. Its altitudinal range in the Pennines takes it up to 2,480 feet near Knock (Wilson 1938).

MOUNTAIN EVERLASTING (*Antennaria dioica*)

Cat's-foot is a charming alternative name for this small plant which may be found on limestone slopes, or occasionally on acid moorland if it is sufficiently rich in nutrients. The leaves, which grow in a rosette, are rimmed and covered below with silvery silky hairs. The flowering shoots give the name cat's-foot; they are covered with white soft hairs. The heads of pinkish florets are surrounded by rather papery bracts—hence, mountain ever-lasting.

It will be noticed that not all the inflorescences are the same shape and colour, some being broader and pale pink, others narrower and deeper pink. The former have male florets and the latter female, and they grow on separate plants. This feature of producing unisexual flowers on different plants is signified by the specific name *dioica*, from the Greek "two houses or dwellings." Another example of a so-called dioecious plant is the marsh valerian (*Valeriana dioica*), which is found in marshy places in the Pennines.

GOLDEN ROD (*Solidago virgaurea*)

Golden Rod, or Aaron's Rod, is not to be confused with the golden rod which has in some areas escaped from cultivated gardens to become established along stream banks at low-level situations. In the *Flora of Westmorland*, Wilson gives its altitude as from 2,000 ft. to 2,400 ft. or higher, and its flowering period as from July to September. He says a form approaching the variety *cambrica* occurs on the rocks by the Lune near Sedbergh and this is the usual form occurring on cliffs at high level.

This plant has now been separated and is recognised as *Solidago virgaurea cambrica*, which is just a variant and not a separate species. The form growing in the fells at up to 1,500 ft. appears to flower much earlier than the flower at lower levels in the Eden Valley. An early record of the plant is from Lawson (1688): "In Cliburn Field, Westmorland, plentifully." It now seems to be a scarce plant at such places, but its golden blooms can still be appreciated growing on some of the sandstone type cliffs in high level sites.

Golden rod is the only European and Asiatic representative of a large North American genus closely related to the asters of cultivated gardens.

CARLINE THISTLE (*Carlina vulgaris*)

This thistle has a range of up to 1,500 ft. It is a limestone plant and can be found down to sites at sea-level. The rosette of leaves of the first season die before the flowering of the plant, which has yellow-brown florets with conspicuous purple-based bracts. These look like rays, and they fold over in wet weather. It is usual to see dead plants from the previous season surviving within the colony, which makes them appear like everlasting types of flowers.

Carline thistles grow to only about nine inches and are used as predictors of the weather. They expand fully in sunshine and close up tightly when it is sunless and wet. They have long been collected for this purpose by country people.

MUSK THISTLE (*Carduus nutans*)

This flower favours limestone. It is recorded by Wilson as growing at 1,350 feet. He gives its habitat as dry pastures and roadsides. Musk is one of our most handsome thistles; it grows up to three feet in height and has large fragrant flowering heads on spineless upper stalks. The plant has a heavy armament of prickles. The colour of the flower is a rich red-purple; white flowers can occur. Old limestone quarries are a good place in which to look for it. At such places, goldfinches feed from the seed-heads.

MELANCHOLY THISTLE (*Cirsium heterophyllum*)

Melancholy thistle is a truly regal plant with its tall straight whitish stems, bearing usually single large heads of purple florets. The odd-sounding name has no relation to the apparent solitariness of the flower heads but comes simply from the fact that a potion from this plant was once used to cure melancholia. The leaves are large and easy to identify even before the plant flowers, having finely prickled margins and a cover of white felted hairs below. They are variously shaped, some being entire (i.e. undivided) and others cut-leaved, giving the plant the specific name of heterophyllum.

Although not a strict calciole, the melancholy thistle is usually found in limestone areas such as open woodland, moist shaded slopes and streamsides.

MARSH ARROWGRASS (*Triglochin palustre*)

An unusual-looking, though quite common, plant in boggy places, the marsh arrowgrass is not a true grass. It was probably named so from its general appearance. The single spike has a number of small rounded flowers with only tiny perianth parts, and at first the conspicuous features are the feathery stigmas. As ripening begins, the fruits lengthen, each consisting of six carpels. Of these, only three are fertile. The ripe fruit splits from below into three parts which hang from the top, giving the appearance of a tiny arrow.

BOG ASPHODEL (*Narthecium ossifragum*)

Bogs, wet moors and acid situations generally are favoured by this plant, which grows on peaty moors to 2,450 feet, higher still on the Northern Pennines. It attains a height of six inches or more and has tough grass-like leaves but a bright yellow flower which is green on the back of the petals. The filaments are densely covered with yellow woolly hairs and the anthers are red. In seed, the plant is also attractive, particularly where it is growing in abundance. The effect, spread over an area, is of deep orange. It is stated in a modern herbal that the plant is poisonous to cows, and that a cat died after drinking the milk of the cow that had been affected.

HERB-PARIS (*Paris quadrifolia*)

Herb-Paris, with a single flower and later a black globular fruit, growing above a ring of normally four broad leaves, is unusual among the monocotyledons in having its flower parts in fours instead of threes. It is a member of the family Trilliaceae, to which belong the Trilliums of cultivation whose flowers are, as expected, tripartite.

The name Paris refers unromantically to the symmetry of parts in fours, from the Latin *pars*; it has apparently no connection with the town, although in France it is claimed as Herbe à Paris or Parisette. This is told by David McClintock in *Companion to Flowers*. He also quotes a more interesting interpretation of the names; should the plant be called after Paris, the son of Priam, King of Troy, then the globular fruit could represent the Apple of Discord and the four leaves stand for Paris and the three goddesses he had to choose from, Hera, Pallas Athene and Aphrodite. Herb-Paris was much used in the past in herbal remedies and Gerrard named it as One-berry or Herbe True-love. He described the leaves as being in "the manner of a Burgundian Crosse or True-love Knot."

In the Pennines, Herb-Paris occurs in woods on calcareous soil and often grows with dog's mercury, among which it is not always easy to spot.

The Northern Pennines. Above: High Cup Nick and Murton Pike. Below:
The confluence of Langdon Beck and the Tees.

Meadow Saxifrage, which occurs among long grass in limestone country.

Ash woodland on limestone.

Plants growing in rocky places. Above: New Zealand Willowherb. Below: Roseroot.

**Two Pennine
Orchids**

**Above: Frog Orchid, which
is no longer found at many
of the lower sites.**

**Right: Broad-leaved
Helleborine, another plant
that is much less common
than it was.**

Bird's-eye Primrose, one of the loveliest of the Pennine flowering plants.

Malham Cove from the air. The limestone scar is one of several majestic features of the Mid-Craven Fault.

Moorland near Haworth. Several good walks can be enjoyed using Haworth as a base.

PENNINE ORCHIDS

About 7,500 species of orchid, of some 450 genera, have been recorded throughout the world. They are mainly of tropical areas, as Colombia in South America, which can boast of over 2,000 species. Europe can muster 125 species and the British Isles 52. A. Wilson (1938) listed only 26 for Westmorland. Of these, only about half were found at an altitude above 800 feet.

Most orchids prefer wet, marshy ground, the type which has been drained and reclaimed in recent years. Here, previously, were to be found marsh, spotted, fragrant and butterfly orchids. Old meadowland and drier situations were suitable for the early purple, frog and burnt-tip orchids and twayblade. The use of artificial manures to boost the growth of grass has choked or poisoned all but remnants of the orchids.

A. Wilson, in *The Flora of Westmorland,* and a supplement to *The North Western Naturalist* on "The Altitudinal Range of British Plants" (1955), gives records for altitude that we have freely quoted. Here are comparisons with present-day records as they apply to the Pennines:

BROAD-LEAVED HELLEBORINE (*Epipactis helleborine*) up to 900 ft. It is now much more rare than it used to be.

NARROW-LEAVED HELLEBORINE (*Cephalanthera ensifolia*) was known at a site at 800 ft. This has always been rare.

COMMON TWAYBLADE (*Listera ovata*) is quoted at 1,350 ft. in North Yorkshire and c. 1,950 ft. in Northumberland but is generally accepted as a lowland plant.

LESSER TWAYBLADE (*L. cordata*) was recorded at 1,800 ft. at Allendale and 1,850 ft. in West Yorkshire but grows down to low levels as a rule.

FROG ORCHID (*Coeloglossum viride*) is found at 1,200 ft. in West Yorkshire and 1,500 ft. in Northumberland. It has gone from many of its lowland sites.

FRAGRANT ORCHID (*Gymnadenia conopsea*) is still fairly common over most of its range up to 1,750 ft.

SMALL-WHITE ORCHID (*Pseudorchis albida*) is another orchid which has become more rare. It used to occur in West Yorkshire to 1,700 feet.

GREATER BUTTERFLY-ORCHID (*Platanthera chlorantha*) and LESSER BUTTERFLY-ORCHID (*P. bifolia*) are still to be found at many of their traditional sites, but they are nowhere as common as of yore. Both are recorded up to the 1,200 ft. contour.

FLY ORCHID (*Ophrys insectifera*) does not have any high-level situations in the Pennines generally, excepting for a record given in the *North West Naturalist* at 1,050 ft.

EARLY-PURPLE ORCHID (*Orchis mascula*) is still fairly widespread and common away from intensively farmed land. It is mentioned up to 1,650 ft. in West Yorkshire.

COMMON SPOTTED-ORCHID (*Dactylorhiza fuchsii*) is frequently found at altitude as quoted from 150—1,600 ft. O.D.

NORTHERN MARSH-ORCHID (*D. purpurella*) is not so common as the other members of the genera and is given a range of 400—850 ft. (Wilson).

HEATH SPOTTED-ORCHID (*D. maculata*) has a range from 20 to 1,500 ft. It hybridises freely with other members of the genus.

BOG ORCHID (*Hammarbya paludosa*) a small insignificant orchid, and can easily be overlooked. It was seen a score of years ago at one of its traditional Pennine sites at 1,000 ft.

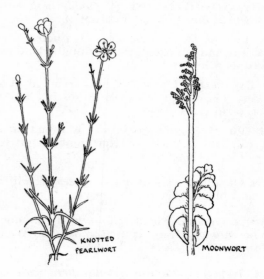

KNOTTED PEARLWORT   MOONWORT

Spore-bearing Plants

OF the four clubmosses listed, Selaginella is the most likely to be discovered; it is usually only a few inches tall and a typical habitat is a limestone flush.

The horsetails (*Equisetum*), present day descendants of the huge Calamites, trees of the coal age forests, have whorls of green jointed branches up the jointed stem. Critical examination of the plants with the help of a book should make the identification not too difficult. The water (*E. fluviatile*), marsh (*E. palustre*) and wood (*E. sylvaticum*) horsetails all produce cones of spores at the top of green shoots, but field horsetail (*E. arvense*) and great or giant horsetail (*E. telmateia*) grow brown spore-bearing shoots in spring followed by green vegetative shoots, those of the latter being like charming miniature pagodas when young. The life history of horsetails is similar to that of ferns outlined below.

As will be noticed, these two groups and the ferns, all reproducing by spores, are not flowering plants, but the ferns, especially, contribute so much to the Pennine floral scene that they are sure to be met with during a flower study expedition.

Ferns are very interesting plants, a subject well worth pursuing, but by a beginner, for the purpose of recognising those likely to be found in the Pennines, the main features of a fern should be understood. It has a two-part life history: the large fern plant is non-sexual and bears a vast number of spores, each of which grows into a minute green heart-shaped plant, called a prothallus, producing male and female organs. After fertilisation, from a female structure on the prothallus, a tiny fern plant begins to grow and eventually becomes the familiar spore-bearing fern. The fern stems are underground and the leafy part, called a frond, grows from a stalk which continues through the frond as the midrib or rachis. If the frond is divided, each section is called a pinna, and this in turn may divide into smaller pinnules. The spores are in spore-cases growing on the underside of the frond in groups known as sori which may have a cover or indusium. For the purpose of identification it is important to examine mature fronds, the shape and position of the sori being often diagnostic.

Four common ferns will be considered first. Their fronds are not easy to describe, yet are easily recognised once the form has been studied with the help of diagrams.

Bracken (*Pteridium aquilinum*) is a fern that spreads over huge areas of acid moorland, within its altitudinal limit, and is distinguished by a long stalk below the branching rachis.

The next two ferns have unfortunate common names, male-fern (*Dryopteris filix-mas*) and lady-fern (*Athyrium filix-femina*). From the information above it will be remembered that the big fern plant is non-sexual and so there is no such thing as a "male fern". These names are believed to date from olden times, at least as far back as Chaucer, before the life history of the fern was known. It was thought then that every plant, like people, had to be either male or female, and the two looked like the opposite sexes of the same plant, the daintier one being designated the lady. In the days of "young men and maidens" this appellation would fit very well. Lady-fern is variable in form. In some plants, the stalk and rachis are green and in others reddish.

The lemon-scented fern (*Thelypteris limbosperma*), found in marshy areas of acid moorland, is distinctive for its yellow-green colour, and the scent of the fronds which have on the underside numerous yellow glands. These are good to observe through a lens, and they glisten beautifully in the sunshine.

Hard fern (*Blechnum spicant*) is another moorland fern which differs from those so far described in having fronds of two types, fertile ones bearing spores of a form giving it the name ladder fern, and sterile vegetative fronds. The pinnae are undivided with those in the middle slightly longer than the rest.

Of a similar plant to hard fern, the frond of polypody (*Polypodium vulgare*) is triangular with longer pinnae at the base, and all fronds bear sori underneath. This fern is found in woods and may grow on trees.

Two interesting ferns forming attractive patches on moist woodland banks of non-limestone areas are the beech fern (*Thelypteris phegopteris*) and oak fern (*Gymnocarpium dryopteris*). They both have a slender stalk and a feathery frond held at right angles to it. The way to distinguish between them is to note that the oak fern rachis is three-branched and the frond broadly triangular, while that of beech fern is narrower and has the two lowest pinnae directed back towards the stalk.

Closely related to the last is limestone fern (*G. robertianum*). The frond can be distinguished by shape from the two above, but a good character to look for is the mealiness on the rachis due to the presence of glands. However, here is a case where the habitat gives the best clue, for, as its name implies, it grows on limestone, particularly on scree where striking patches of this fern may be seen.

A fern of similar situations to the last is brittle bladder-fern (*Cystopteris fragilis*), one with a very delicate frond. Each sorus is covered by a hooded indusium which looks like a tiny bladder when young. Brittle bladder-fern may also be found on limestone walls, and other ferns of this habitat are the spleenworts—black (*Asplenium adiantum-nigrum*), maidenhair (*A. trichomanes*), green (*A. viride*) and rue-leaved (*A. rutamuraria*), and rusty black (*Ceterach officinarium*). Green spleenwort with a green rachis is less common than maidenhair spleenwort (rachis black) and should be searched for in deeper crevices.

Sometimes ferns of limestone walls are dispersed and become established in the mortar of gritstone walls where there is a supply of lime. I have seen brittle bladder-fern flourishing on river bridges well away from limestone country. An interesting comment regarding conservation is that some of the small ferns of rocky places have become scarce from the depradations of past collectors, but that man has in some measure made up for it by providing a similar artificial habitat, the walls he has built.

Hart's-tongue fern (*Phyllitis scolopendrium*), with its straplike shiny undivided fronds, is generally familiar. It prefers shady places. Perhaps its most attractive setting is in the grikes of limestone pavements. The arrangement of the long sori makes them look like the legs of a centipede and is responsible for the specific name.

All the ferns in the list, except the last two, are of the so-called crozier or fiddle-head type whose fronds come up from the ground coiled, and uncurl as they develop. Of the other type are moonwort (*Botrychium lunaria*) and adder's-tongue fern (*Ophioglossum vulgatum*). Apart from the magic once associated with them, they are interesting botanically. Unlike the other ferns they have a non-green prothallus underground, and a fleshy rootstock sending up very few shoots, straight, not coiled, each of which produces a leaf-like frond and a fertile frond. Among the grasses, neither species is easy to find, yet if one is spotted, there may be several more. Although these ferns do not form clumps, the single plants may be scattered over quite a wide area.

More Difficult Identification

THIS chapter could be called a cautionary tale. We hope it will also be an encouragement to the beginner who may be somewhat perplexed by the large number of species in the list of plants coming between the ferns of the previous chapter and the rushes, sedges and grasses of the next. A number of these have already been discussed; among the others it is often hard to decide which species may be safely named from the flower book and which require expert help in identification. Be encouraged for the first, and use caution for the second!

It is not possible here to explain distinguishing features of all these species; we aim to give a few general guide-lines.

A systematic approach is always advisable, and it is useful to learn the main features of the larger plant families, for example, Umbelliferae, Labiatae, Compositae. Sometimes the genus is easily recognisable, such as Myosotis, Veronica and Galium. Where a genus contains a large number of species, the use of a key in a Flora is a more straightforward procedure than reading through all the descriptions in a more popular book. By either method, experience will be gained and it is worth remembering the value of personal aids to memory for use in the field.

If the plant examined does not concur in every respect with the description of the species, the identification may still be correct as long as the flower structure tallies; the vegetative part of the plant may vary owing to an unusual habitat. For example, a specimen may grow exceptionally tall if surrounded by high-growing vegetation. More important deviations from the normal characteristics (in the flowers and/or the rest of the plant) will be observed if the plant found is a variety of the species, or a subspecies, or a hybrid with a related species. An example of each is given by:

Rumex sanguineus var. *viride*, the more green variety of red-veined dock which is much commoner than var. *sanguineus; Viola riviniana* ssp. *minor* which has smaller leaves than ssp. *riviniana*, the common dog violet, and false oxlips, which are hybrids between cowslips and primroses, scientifically known as *Primula veris* x *vulgaris*. The botanist should acquire familiarity with the pure species before proceeding far in this line of flower study.

Keeping to the systematic order of flowering plants, we now list a selection of genera to be approached with caution but providing aspects of study within the scope of the beginner.

Rubus

This genus includes cloudberry, stone bramble and raspberry, all easily named, but also the brambles or blackberries belonging to an aggregate species embracing a large number of individual species that certainly need expert identification. Any brambles found are best recorded as *Rubus fruticosus* agg.

Alchemilla

Alchemilla vulgaris agg., the name used in the list, includes all the British species of the genus except alpine lady's-mantle and the rare *A. conjuncta*. The leaf characters are good for identifying the *A. vulgaris* species and may be used for the three most likely to be met with in the Pennines, namely: *A. xanthochlora* with hairs on the lower leaf surface but almost none above (feeling like "kid gloves on top"); *A. glabra*, having no hairs on the leaf and the whole plant smooth or glabrous, and *A. vestita*, a species hairy all over ("woolly vest"). In Teesdale, where Dr. Bradshaw has recorded nine species of *Alchemilla*, and in Craven, the rarer species of the genus may be found, so that in these places the plants need careful examination.

Rosa

Hybrids among the roses are frequently found. If not hybridised, the field rose (*Rosa arvensis*) and burnet rose (*R. pimpinellifolia*) have distinct characteristics. It is usually possible to separate dog rose (*R. canina*) — an extremely variable species — and its hybrids from the downy rose group (*R. villosa* agg.) and hybrids.

Salix

This is a difficult genus, further complicated by possessing separate male and female plants as well as hybridisation. It is useful to discover which willows have early catkins and which produce catkins along with the leaves. Very likely willows will be found that can be assigned to a species, or to be very near to that species, but further complications are best left to the specialist.

The male plants of *Salix caprea* are often called pussy willow in spring from the appearance of the catkins; it is also known as "palm" from its use in churches in Palm Sunday in the absence of the true palm in Britain. *S. repens* can be easily distinguished from other willows by its low-growing and creeping habit.

The family Compositae

The plants in this family are easy enough to pick out from others because the inflorescence consists of heads of florets surrounded by bracts, but of all its members the yellow-flowered ones provide the biggest stumbling block for the beginner. They are sometimes dismissed as far too hard, but this need not be so once the "possibles" are separated from the "impossibles".

Cat's-ear (*Hypochoeris radicata*) is a common plant, normally with the stem forking to give two heads of florets and tiny bracts (the cat's ears?) on the stem. Rough hawkbit (*Leontodon hispidus*) is superficially similar, but a rougher plant with single heads and the hairs on the leaves are forked. The smaller, autumnal hawkbit (*L. autumnalis*), is a smoother plant.

The hawkweeds (*Hieracium* spp.) and hawk's-beards (*Crepis* spp.) can be distinguished by closely examining their bracts and fruits, for which reference to a Flora should be made for details. Once this obstacle has been overcome, the smooth and marsh hawk's-beards (*C. capillaris* and *C. paludosa*) may be recognised. *Hieracium* is acknowledged to be the most difficult genus in the British flora as regards naming and study of the species. Happily the charming mouse-ear hawkweeds (*H. pilosella*) with lemon-yellow florets, the outer tinged red below, and rosette of leaves white underneath with long white hairs, may be distinguished from the rest by the beginner. Identification of the other *Hieracia* must be confirmed by an expert.

With the help of a Flora, dandelions (*Taraxacum* spp.) may be divided into four main groups or aggregates: common dandelion (*T. officinalis*), within which are many forms; narrow-leaved marsh dandelion (*T. palustre*); broad-leaved marsh dandelion (*T. spectabile*), and lesser dandelion (*T. laevigatum*).

The lesser dandelion may be found in dry sandy or calcareous places in the Pennines.

We hope that from the foregoing the reader will have some idea of the problems in identification, but at the same time realise that not all the difficulties are insurmountable.

ALTHOUGH some sedges and some grasses are difficult to identify, this is not the case for all members of the families to which they belong; quite a number of the common species may easily be named.

The family *Cyperaceae* includes a number of "rush-like sedges", along with the genus *Carex*, the true sedges. Among the first group, the two cotton grasses of acid bogs on the moors are most easily recognised in fruit with their conspicuous cottony heads, *Eriophorum angustifolium* being the common or many-headed cotton grass, and hare's-tail (*E. vaginatum*) having a single tuft of fruits. In deergrass (*Scirpus caespitosus*) and common spike-rush (*Eleocharis palustris*) the brown flowers form a small cone-shaped head at the top of a leafless stalk; the former is often found in abundance on acid moorland, whilst the latter is a common plant of wet places. The minute bristle club-rush (*Scirpus setaceus*) should be searched for in slow streams and ditches. Flat-sedge (*Blysmus compressus*), in boggy places, has—as its name implies—a flattened inflorescence; this is rich brown in colour with a bronze sheen.

It will be noticed that the members of *Cyperaceae* do not have sepals or petals and the tiny flowers grow in close heads or spikes. *Carex* is by far the largest genus in the family and is well repre-sented in the Pennines. The carices or true sedges have grass-like leaves with a blade and a leaf base forming a sheath round the stem. This is solid and in many sedges triangular in section. The inflorescence consists of unisexual flowers, that is, separate male and female flowers; in all species but one they occur on the same plant. The exception is a tiny sedge of limestone bogs, *Carex dioica*, the dioecious or separate-headed sedge.

In the rest (which are monoecious) the male and female flowers may grow together as mixed spikes, or form separate spikes, in which case the males are usually above the females.

In addition to the inflorescence, and of course the vegetative structure, two features which are important in identifying sedges are the glumes (one below each flower) and the ripe fruit. Young specimens should not be relied on for naming until the species is thoroughly known. One of the best references for these two features is in the Collins Pocket Guide which gives diagrams of all the fruits and female glumes.

If a start is made with the more distinctive common species, the beginner gains confidence and will find that after all some of the sedges are not too difficult to name. Here are three:

Common sedge (*Carex nigra*) is a common and widespread species, and although it is very variable in form, two useful characters are the black or very dark female glumes with a pale midrib not reaching the tip, and the two stigmas (three stigmas are commoner in sedges).

Hairy sedge (*C. hirta*) is distinguished by its hairy leaves and leaf sheaths, and the green fruits which are also hairy. It is another common sedge, found in damp places amongst grass and in woods.

Star sedge (*C. echinata*) has mixed spikes, and as the fruits ripen they tend to spread, giving each spike a starry appearance. It is very common in acid bogs.

Of the smaller sedges, one of the nicest to find, in base-rich bogs and flushes, is flea sedge (*C. pulicaris*); the shiny brown fruits really do look like fleas and when ripe "jump" off if touched. The flowers here are in a single spike, male at the top and female below.

Pill sedge (*C. pilulifera*)—literally "pill-bearing", is also a small species living up to its name in the shape of its fruits. This is a sedge of drier, more acid areas.

Another small one is spring-sedge (*C. caryophyllea*), common in limestone grassland. It flowers early and the abundant pale yellow anthers on the male spike are conspicuous, although other features should be checked with the flower book or Flora for certain identification.

With the help of a Flora, more difficult species in the list could be usefully paired or grouped and notes tabulated for use in the field, especially if the similarities between a pair are at first sight more obvious than their differences, for instance carnation sedge (*C. panicea*) and glaucous sedge (*C. flacca*). In the case of long-stalked yellow-sedge (*C. lepidocarpa*) and common yellow-sedge (*C. demissa*) the habitat helps, as the first grows in basic and the other in acid bogs.

Pennine Grasses

GRASSES all belong to the family *Gramineae*. They have hollow cylindrical stems, prominently marked by the nodes which are thickened as a ring at the base of each leaf sheath. At the top of the sheath is an outgrowth called the ligule and from here continues the leaf blade. In several species the shape of the ligule is an important distinguishing feature.

The flowers of grasses are hermaphrodite, having three stamens and two feathery stigmas, and are of a specialised form best examined in one of the larger species. But many are easy to identify without reference to detailed structure. The variety of shape in the glumes which enclose the flowers in spikelets, the presence or absence of awns, and the different branching and shapes of the inflorescences found in the large number of species of the family all contribute to their individual characteristics.

The common names of grasses are often graphic descriptions, as illustrated by the following:

The inflorescence of cock's-foot (*Dactylis glomerata*) when inverted to touch a flat surface looks like the spread toes of a cockerel; crested dog's-tail (*Cynosurus cristatus*) can be made to wag; timothy or cat's-tail (*Phleum pratense*) has a rougher look and feel than the softer silky spike of meadow foxtail (*Alopecurus pratensis*), and quaking-grass (*Briza media*) has many slender-stalked little brown inflorescences which quiver in the wind.

Other species with colour, other than green, in the inflorescence are purple moor-grass (*Molinia caerulea*) of acid bogs, and blue moor-grass (*Sesleria caerulea*) of limestone grassland, whilst the two melicks, of shady places (*Melica uniflora* and *M. nutans*) have delicate purplish brown glumes. The latter of these two is known as mountain melick and is typical of limestone woodland.

In purple moor-grass, the ligule is replaced by a ring of hairs, as also in heath-grass (*Sieglingia decumbens*), a useful check for this species.

Some moorland grasses, such as Yorkshire-fog (*Holcus lanatus*) and mat-grass (*Nardus stricta*) are quite distinctive, but the bents

(*Agrostis spp.*) and fescues (*Festuca spp.*) although common may give more difficulty. It is also more difficult to identify grasses by their vegetative features than by the flowers, but with practice and careful observation this can be done.

We hope that the foregoing will encourage the reader to make a step-by-step beginning on the identification of sedges and grasses which, with the help of reliable and well illustrated books, can lead to a very rewarding study.

FLEA SEDGE

BLUE MOOR GRASS

Plant Lore

THE idea that every living creature and plant upon the Earth is there for some purpose, a common belief, must have resulted in much experimentation in testing the virtues of all kinds of flowering plants. If the fruit of the plant was of no avail, then the stem, leaves or root could all be tried. The old herbalists deduced that if a plant resembled a particular organ then it would be useful for that organ's treatment. The violet, with heart-shaped leaves, was good for the heart, lungwort for the lungs, eye-bright for the eyes.

The modern names for many plants give clues to their usage. Butterbur's huge leaves were used to wrap up butter for the market before the days of paper; dyers greenweed was used for dyeing, and goutweed to cure the gout. Bedstraw was the forerunner to the feather bed, and whitlow grass became a cure for whitlows.

Today, many such plants may appear to be more plentiful at high levels on account of depredations, caused by their popularity, in the more accessible lowland areas. In the valleys, agricultural practice and urbanisation have destroyed many sites where herbs grew.

A check-list has been attempted of the plants that have been documented as useful. The main sources of many such records were the *Herbals* of Gerard (1597) and Parkinson (1629), but many other records have been used. Notes have been acquired from personal knowledge and communication with the Pennine folks.

LESSER CELANDINE takes its name from the Greek name for swallow, the flowering period coinciding with the visit of the swallows, which were thought to restore the sight of their young by its use.

WOOD ANEMONE (Thunder Flower) was infused as a tea for external use only, such as the washing of ulcers and sores. It was also used as an eyewash.

61

Marsh Marigold (King Cup) produced a yellow dye, extracted after the petals were boiled with alum. The buds can be pickled in the same way as capers.

Green Hellebore (Felling Grass) is still found surviving around farmsteads, particularly those that are derelict. It was used by the old cow-doctors who performed the operation on unthrifty cattle of "cutting them for the felling." This entailed making an incision through the beast's dewlap and threading in it a bacon-rind entwined with sprigs of green hellebore. This was firmly secured with the belief that the "bad humours" of the unthrifty beast would be "drawn" to drip away at the incision. This treatment could take up to three weeks—if the patient had not succumbed before that time. This plant was also used by witches to bring on hallucination and hysterical conditions.

Baneberry (Herb Christopher) is a poisonous plant which yields a black dye.

Greater Celandine was credited with having sedative, purgative and diuretic powers. It also was a common cure for warts, being readily applied by breaking the stem and smearing the fresh juice.

Poppy juice was used to cure warts. Pillows were stuffed with dried poppy plants and their narcotic properties were said to promote sleep.

Water Cress, frequently found growing at high altitudes, became a salad plant. High sites were preferred to lowland sites, there being less risk of contamination at undisturbed places.

Scurvy Grass was named because it was a cure for scurvy. The seaside type was that readily available to seamen. Before oranges were the main source of vitamin C, it is likely that this plant was generally used to offset vitamin deficiency.

Sweet Violet. The leaves were said to have antiseptic properties and, along with the flowers, were thought helpful to the kidneys. The rhizomes have emetic properties. A tea made from the plant was a cure for insomnia, cardiac disorders and gout. The sweet violet was given the testimony as a panacea, but other species of *Viola* are given some credits.

Wild Pansy was a cure for eczema. An unpleasant drink was concocted from it as a cure for catarrhal conditions.

Milkwort has been used to promote expectoration and as a cough cure.

St. John's Wort seems to have been a most useful herb, but we cannot find which species of the plant was of most importance. As a herb, it was blended with various vegetable juices to give valuable applications to cuts, sores and rheumatic limbs and swellings. Bunches hung in windows discouraged spells on the Eve of St. John's Day, June 24. If the eyes were rubbed with the dew obtained from the plant on that morning they were said to be preserved from disease. Other uses of the plant were as a cough cure and to prevent young children from bed-wetting. Gerard maintained that an oil obtained from the leaves had valuable antiseptic properties and should be applied to wounds caused by a venomous weapon. Even in modern times an ointment has been prepared from the leaves and flowers, mixed with olive-oil, for the relief of bed-sores.

Cranesbill. We fail to trace which species was credited with the ability to stop bleeding from a cut and which would make a drink against cholera.

Holly. As well as its usefulness as a fencing agent, and its decorative use at Christmas, holly was at one time in demand by bird-catchers to manufacture birdlime.

Gorse. Drinks made from the flowers were said to cleanse the liver and relieve jaundice. It was a favourite, mixed with onion peel, for the dyeing of pasche eggs (it also gave the eggs a pleasant flavour). The scientific name for needle furze is *Genista* meaning "knee"!

Rest Harrow may not have any specific usage, but its name is of interest, being a derivation from the Greek word meaning an ass. The roots of the plant, being matted, brought the ass-drawn plough to a standstill.

Red Clover has a greater honey-content than white clover, but it is not so readily available to the bees. A syrup was made to ease whooping cough. It was used in medicines for the treatment of skin complaints.

White Clover is extensively used in grass-seed mixture for the purpose of enriching the soil in nitrogen.

Blackthorn. The broken nuts of the fruit have been used to make a form of liquor known as sloe gin. The stems of blackthorn are much sought after for walking sticks.

Cherry has made its reputation as a table fruit and is much famed for making walking sticks.

Meadow Sweet. European peasants made decoctions and infusions of willow for relief of toothache, gout, rheumatism and earache, but it was from meadow sweet that the secret of salacin, a constituent of meadow sweet, was found which had a real effect upon such complaints. According to Gerard, its leaves excelled all others for "strewing" to deck up houses. The flowers were used for flavouring beverages and making a herbal tea.

WOOD AVENS (Herb Bennet) had medicinal properties and was used for seasoning in place of cloves. It was thought to dispel raw humours from the belly.

WATER AVENS (Bachelor's Button) was considered to be a preventative against plague.

CINQUEFOIL was an ingredient of "flying ointment", which witches rubbed over their bodies, along with other ingredients, to give them the power of flight. Concoctions made from it were a powerful bait for fish.

AGRIMONY. The translation of the name from its Greek origin proves it to have been used to cure cataract of the eye. A drink made from it had a taste similar to apricot. Culpeper gave it as a cure for gout and bruised joints when applied to them "... and mixed with swines grease it helpeth old sores ... it draweth forth thorns and splinters of wood, nails and any other such things gotten into the flesh." It was also believed to be an antidote for snake-bite.

SALAD BURNET. Parkinson and Culpeper stated that its leaves were used in salads, and even in recent times have been declared to be delicious with cheese in a sandwich. It was used to flavour claret and other drinks. Its scientific name is of interest, *Poterium* —being "a drinking cup", and *sanguisorba*—"stopping the flow of blood."

GREATER BURNET has been used to make a wine popular with country people.

DOG ROSE, AND OTHER WILD ROSES. The former is said to live longer than all wild plants. Rose-hips are well known for the making of a vitamin C rich syrup, popular during the 1939-45 war and for some time afterwards remembered. Hips and petals were used against catarrh, bronchitis and even pulmonary disorders. It is also considered to be a useful tranquilliser.

ROWAN berries were used in remedies against influenza and sore throats. It was thought to combat difficiency diseases affecting skin and neural health. Rowan was used as a preserve and was fermented for a drink. The bark was used for tanning and the wood for turning.

HAWTHORN. A useful herbal drink made from the leaves was considered good for rheumatic and cardine disorders. It was claimed that taking the drink or the leaves regularly would prolong life. It was unlucky to take it indoors.

ROSEROOT. A distilled water was obtained from the dried roots; it had a definite but diluted scent of rose-water. Roseroot was used for the complexion and to sprinkle over clothes before the days of dry-cleaning and over-washing. The plant was known as midsummer men. Girls would set it up in their homes on Midsummer's Eve and test their lovers' fidelity by the length of time it flourished.

ORPINE, like house-leek, was hung over doorways as a charm against lightning and to scare away witches. It was also a love charm.

BITING STONECROP had, according to Pliny, the reputation of producing sleep. It must be wrapped in a black cloth and put under the pillow unawares. It was also considered good for dropsy.

HOUSELEEK. On account of the belief that it counteracted witchcraft and lightning there were local antipathies against uprooting it. It was a cure for warts. A recent book by Kenneth Alsop gives an account of his successful treatment of a wart with a concoction made from this plant. I can remember seeing it used as a cure for wind galls on horse's legs. The fractured leaves were rubbed on the galls.

SUNDEW was said to remove warts and corns; it was once used as a tincture.

SAXIFRAGE, of which there are many species, acquires its name from *saxum* (stone) and *frango* (I break), and according to Pliny the plant was used to break up gall-stones within the human body.

ENCHANTER'S NIGHTSHADE. We can find no references to the usage of this plant, but its name suggests that it must have had a connection with the necromancers of old.

HEMLOCK was a bad poison but had some useful medicinal properties, both sedative and analgesic. Its leaves were at times used for poultices.

GOUTWEED (Ground Elder) was used in herbal remedies, being eaten as salad or vegetable.

BURNET SAXIFRAGE was another "stonebreaker", as was also

PEPPER SAXIFRAGE. If this was eaten by milking cows it gave an unpleasant taste to the milk.

SWEET CICELY, with its myrrh-like smell, was popular in salads and boiled as a substitute for spinach. The roots were boiled and served with white sauce, while its seeds were ground and mixed with wax to rub on furniture, leaving a perfume.

EARTH NUT was a popular item with children. They dug up and ate the root, which they called yow-yaw nut.

COW PARSNIP, both fruit and leaf, have been used in a concoction as a sedative.

SPIGNEL MEU undoubtedly had local uses. It was known as The Westmorland Herb.

WILD ANGELICA was a cure for tummy ache and also to expel wind. It counteracted spells and witchcraft. The species used as cake decoration is imported from Denmark.

IVY. A mild infusion was considered to be good for combating catarrh, gout and rheumatism, being a purgative. The leaves made a poultice for slow-healing wounds.

ELDER. Wine, made both from the berries and the flowers, are popular country beverages. It was planted around homesteads to protect them against witches. A soothing ointment was made from the inner green bark. Elderberry tea may still be used in some country places as a hot cordial to alleviate bronchial congestion. Bruised elder-leaves were effective for protecting fruit and vegetables, acting as an insecticide against greenfly and aphids. It was also used as an additive to various concoctions.

WOODRUFF was hung to keep rooms cool in hot weather. It remained fragrant through the year and was greatly used for strewing. It acted as a deterrent against moths. Leaves were placed in pocket watches for their fragrance. Woodruff stuffed mattresses and pillows. A stimulating tea infused from it purified the blood.

YELLOW LADY'S BEDSTRAW was used as a substitute for rennet to curdle milk. Its root produced a red dye.

VALERIAN. The root of this plant had sedative properties, being used to treat hysteria and as a vervine. A bitter, foul-smelling tonic was a cure-all in parts of England. In the North, it was a kitchen requisite for broth. The root was adored by rats, and catchers used it as a bait.

GOLDEN-ROD. A tea made from this plant improves digestion. It was favoured for the treatment of bronchitis and tuberculosis.

MOUNTAIN EVERLASTING combated throat infections.

COLTSFOOT could be made up into a cough-cure. We have seen it smoked by tramps in the absence of tobacco.

BUTTERBUR had its place before paper was used to wrap butter.

MUSK THISTLE was thought to protect buildings from being struck by lightning.

CARLINE THISTLE. The root in autumn is rich in active chemicals which can be prepared into a herbal tonic. The species takes its name from Charlemagne, to whom its medicinal properties were revealed.

BURDOCK was a constituent of a herb drink, being used along with dandelion, which was said to be very good for the blood.

CHICORY, an alien in Britain, has been used for various purposes, the best known being as a forage plant. Was also used as a salad component.

HAWKWEED. The scientific word is *Hieracium,* from the Greek *hierax* (a hawk). There was a belief that hawks used the plant to clear their sight.

DANDELION has many uses, its leaves going into salads or being cooked like spinach. Beer is brewed from the leaves, and wine from the flowers. "Coffee" comes from roots rich in insulin. Dandelion can give treatment as a mild laxative and tummy-settler. The fresh green leaves encourage the function of the gall-bladder.

BILBERRY makes a preserve which is appetising and has anti-diorrhea properties. It is also the source of a blue dye.

COWBERRY has similar uses but is also effective against rheumatic disorders.

CRANBERRY, which can be sought in some high-level bogs, goes with venison and, of course, turkey. Doubtless the cranberry sauce we get in Britain is imported; the wild form in this country is too sparsely distributed to be gathered commercially.

HEATHER, a tranquillizer, is best applied by eating the heather honey. The scientific name, *Calluna*, is derived from the Greek name for "a broom".

PRIMROSE was at one time cultured for its sweetening qualities. The leaves can be used to treat cuts and wounds. Flowers boiled gently make a drink to drive out worms and relieve several rheumatic ailments.

COWSLIP is not mentioned for much other than aesthetic qualities, but cowslip wine has been a well-known beverage in Cumbria. A cream made from cowslip was said to be a cure for wrinkles.

CENTAURY was greatly valued, as its name—meaning 100 gold pieces—implies. It was used as an infusion in wine and has fever-reducing properties.

THE GENTIANS. Gentian tea was recommended for digestion, keeping out the cold and killing germs. A person one of the authors knew made his gentian tea from field gentian.

COMFREY was often to be found in or close to the kitchen garden. It was commonly known as knitbone, giving some inference of its use. It was applied to sprains, which quickly improved (despite or on account of the treatment).

GREATER BINDWEED is known for its purgative properties.

WOODY NIGHTSHADE (Bitter Sweet) was a useful herb, though its berries are poisonous. It was used for both skin-troubles and coughs.

IVY-LEAVED TOADFLAX was eaten as a salad plant. The taste is acrid and pungent.

FOXGLOVE is a heart medicine and can be a life-saving drug. Gerarde, in his Herbal, said: "Yet they are of no use, neither have they any place amongst medicines according to the ancients".

EYEBRIGHT spp., as their name implies, were of use as an eye tonic.

YELLOW RATTLE was used as an eye cure and for the yellow dye it produces.

THE MINTS. Various mints were used medicinally and for flavouring. An oil for massaging was made from the leaves.

FIELD MINT. Culpeper suggests the use of hot rose petals and mint applied to the head as a cure for sleeplessness. Mint leaves added to a bath can relax the body. Bees will never leave a hive that has first been rubbed with corn mint, and corn mint placed amongst cheeses will preserve them from corruption. Pliny refers to mint as a stimulant to appetite. It would not suffer milk in the stomach to wax sour.

MARJORAM. The dried leaves moistened and placed in a muslin bag brought instant relief when used as a fermentation and applied to rheumatic parts of the body. It was also used for flavouring, perfumery and as a tea. Marjoram makes a reddish-brown dye and can relieve strains and bruises. It flavoured egg-dishes, potatoes, mushrooms and milk-puddings. One of the authors remembers it best as a tasty ingredient to flavour home-made sausage. It cured asthmatical and bronchial coughs.

WILD THYME. Oil of Thyme is distilled from the fresh leaves and flowers. One of its chief elements is thymol, a strong anti-septic. Parkinson wrote: "There is no herb of more use in the house high or low ... for bathing, for strewing, to make sauces for fish and flesh." It was also a remedy for depression, and has for centuries been used with other herbs in herb butters and herb vinegars.

SELF-HEAL was reported to cure many disorders, fevers and wounds. It was an antidote for a disease common among soldiers in garrisons which brought about an inflammation of mouth, tongue and throat. Today it is a tonic and astringent, also a gargle when the fresh herb in May is infused with boiling water.

GROUND IVY was used in herbal remedies, and as a tonic and vermifuge.

BETONY had a reputation as a medicinal plant, and was used to make both a tea and a medicinal tobacco.

HEDGE WOUNDWORT. Gerarde tells how a farm-worker cut his leg to the bone when scything; it healed within a week after he applied the leaves.

Good King Henry was eaten as a spinach and called "markery". It cured wounds and cleared old ulcers. Another name "smiddy leaves", relates to the fact it was found growing near the smithy. It was a useful antidote for burns and cuts.

Bistort (Easter-May Giants, Easter Ledges). These have been used for herb pudding right up to modern times.

Stinging Nettle was often mixed with bistort as an ingredient for herb pudding. It was considered to be good for debility and for those with a tendency to tuberculosis.

Alpine Bistort has edible underground stems.

Butter Dock was used in salads. It was pulled and eaten by children. Used on milk, it formed a junket.

Yarrow was reputed to be a great healer of the human body, tackling colds, coughs, fevers and blood disorders. Known as "carpenter's weed", it was useful in stopping the flow of blood from cuts and wounds. A pleasant drink could be made from it. Culpeper claimed "that it stayed the shedding of the hair, the head being bathed with the concoction of it."

Feverfew had well-known properties for curing agues and fevers. It gives instant relief to insect bites.

Docks sp. The grub growing at the base of the root was considered by anglers to be a sure killer.

Daphne Mezereon, a blistering agent, was used in liniments and for the treatment of certain types of ulcers.

Sweet Gale produces myrtle wax when treated with hot water. This wax was used to polish furniture and to make candles which had a resinous odour and a clear white flame. Sweet gale was also a cure for the itch.

Early Purple Orchis made into a beverage known as "salop". This was a popular drink in Tudor times and later, "Salop houses" becoming popular. Here the drink was taken in the manner of coffee today.

Hazel, famed for edible nuts, was also favoured for making hurdles, wattles, small articles and walking sticks.

Bay Willow was employed in basket-making and also for hurdles and ropes. It was in use before quinine, a medicine being made from the bark.

Lily-of-the-Valley is a plant with a therapeutical scent that is said to be a memory restorative. It contains a drug allied to digitalis, which is non-poisonous and considered good for the restoration of speech following cardiac arrest.

RAMSONS (Wood Garlic) was used for flavouring and, worn in the socks, as a cure for colds and rheumatism.

BOG ASPHODEL. The ground on which it grows is considered to be no good for running sheep.

SOFT RUSH was favoured for thatch and strewing. The Rush-bearings in Cumbria signify the gathering and strewing of the rushes in churches. The pith of this rush was used for candle-wicks. Ropes made from rushes would be used for fastening the thatch on to house roofs and haystacks.

WILD ARUM (Lords and Ladies). The purple-headed plants were Lords and the white specimens were Ladies. Although the berries were poisonous, the starchy tubers were a source of food.

JUNIPER is not as common on the Pennines as in Lakeland, but a little occurs. From it was made cade oil, a cure for skin disorders such as psoriasis.

SWEET VERNAL GRASS grows to a high altitude and is eaten by sheep, though considered to be too bitter for cattle. It was erroneously recommended in seeds mixtures 150 years ago and has kept finding its place in them since. It is recognised by its early flowering.

TIMOTHY is a valuable forage grass from an American source. Its seed was sent to England in 1760. It does very well on peaty soil where there is high rainfall.

BROWN BENT GRASS is frequent and grows on Little Dun Fell to 2,700 ft. It is not favoured as a forage grass.

WAVY-HAIR GRASS, abundant among the heather, provides grazing for sheep.

TUFTED-HAIR GRASS, a useless fodder, is nonetheless very decorative.

YORKSHIRE FOG, a useless forage grass, grows over much land that could grow better grass.

MAT GRASS, another useless grass, is eaten only when it is quite young. It is attacked by the caterpillar of the antler moth, and in some years there are vast swarms of their larvae.

RYE GRASS, which can be common up to 1,400 ft., and is one of the most useful grasses.

SHEEP'S FESCUE is sought by both sheep and cattle. There are many common and variable forms. It forms a large portion of the turf of many hillsides.

CRESTED DOG'S TAIL is only grazed in its young stages. The fine stems have been much used for the plaiting of straw hats.

COMMON QUAKING GRASS, which grows on poor soil, is too bitter to be a favoured fodder, but is very decorative.

ANNUAL MEADOW GRASS. Very common to the highest altitudes, it is early flowering even in the most inhospitable places.

SMOOTH MEADOW GRASS has a creeping rootstock. As a quick coloniser it deters better types of grasses.

PURPLE MOOR GRASS is of no agricultural value but its long straws are said to have been used by country people to make stiff carpet brushes. Twisted together, they make a strong durable line.

BLUE MOOR GRASS is an early flowering grass of little use except for its attractive appearance.

SPHAGNUM MOSS. Various species have been used. In the 1914-18 war it was in demand to use as dressings for wounds.

MOONWORT. In *Wayside and Woodland Ferns*, by Edward Step (1922) it is stated: "It was credited with being an efficient aid to the burglar of the period, and to all those who were under the constraint of bolts or bars. If moonwort could be obtained and applied to the lock, the latter would at once cease to be a fastening. Even the shoes nailed on the feet of horses that might venture across the heath where moonwort grew would be affected and fall off." Du Bartes, in his *Divine Weekes* has a reference to this reputed quality of the fern. This belief was widespread.

BRACKEN is a great scourge on the Pennines. Various ways have been tried to eradicate it. It is hoped that chemicals used will be selective and not do harm to other useful plants.

THE SPLEENWORTS are named from being a medicine for the spleen and the liver, "as well as in all other griefes proceedings of oppilations stoppings whatsoever".

MALE FERN is the species around which centres much delightful nonsense. Fern-seed conferred invisibility if obtained on St. John's Eve by the careful observance of certain precautions. It had a place in the pharmocopaeia as an anthelmintic.

FIELD HORSETAIL causes intestinal irritations and even loss in cattle grazing on it.

Where to Go

ANYONE who is interested in Pennine plants and also birds has the added pleasure of making observations in which both can be closely related. One of the authors has combined both interests for over half a century. As an example, the ring ouzel breeds in a variety of habitats, such as ledges on cliffs or escarpments on peaty slopes, in heather or rushes, in mineshafts and potholes. Old buildings are used. Some pairs build their nests in trees, mainly rowan and pine. Stone walls are favoured by other ring ouzels.

Nests may be re-used over a number of years, and at such nests may be found floral decoration. Ring ouzels, adapting previously used sites for their second brood, often return to breed at the same site in subsequent years, and over the course of several seasons a rich fertility is created from the litter. This prompts a luxurious vegetation around the nest. Such plants as wood-sorrel, lady's mantle, bilberry and green spleenwort take advantage of such fertile spots and give embellishment to the nest of *Turdus torquatos*. When searching round many of the mountain gills one may see other good plant habitats where mosses and ferns abound.

The buzzard, another bird species found on the high Pennines, takes sprigs of greenery, usually of rowan, to its nest. Birch, Scots pine and ash have also been noted.

Interesting plants can be found growing on the edge of high-lying footpaths throughout the Pennines. On northern stretches one might see New Zealand willowherb, blinks, felwort, spring cinquefoil, even hairy stonecrop. Trampling can be detrimental to most plants, but rock-rose thrives well under trampling and rough treatment. Not all plants are so hardy, and walkers (particularly when in parties) should take care where they step even when following well-known trails and footpaths. Walkers on such popular routes as the Pennine Way have significantly widened the path. Motorised vehicles, both cars and cycles, are seen increasingly on the fells to the detriment of some good plant habitats.

If there is toleration and discussion between the conflicting interests, a solution can usually be found.

New plants have been introduced by way of the seeds being carried inadvertently on footwear or clothing. An instance of this kind at a lower elevation, about 600 feet, was proved when mousetail (*Myosurus minimus*) was found growing on the site of Brough Hill Fair. The seeds had presumably been carried from the heaths of southern England by the gypsies who hold an annual fair there. The seed was probably scattered by ponies that had been grazing the southern heaths.

Unusual plants may be introduced accidentally anywhere in the Pennine region. Sometimes an alien plant is quickly established. The New Zealand willowherb is a case in point. Accidental introductions are of interest, but not those brought about on purpose. A misguided ornithologist deliberately scattered the seeds of sedges, rushes and various other plants to attract birds to suitable sites.

The spread of "exotic" plants can be traced to several different sources. The firms selling commercial bird seed and cattle feeding-stuffs import grain that can hold the seeds of alien plants. Weed seed adheres to the fleeces of sheep taken to the urban mills. Garden escapes may be robust in new habitats. High-lying farmsteads that become derelict often send emissaries from the garden, and snowdrops and daffodils, polyanthus, colourful primulas, gooseberry and flowering currant are good examples of the modern escapes.

The sides of high-level passes of the Pennines support plants grown from seeds that fell from forage crops being transported on lorries. Chicory has spread in this way, and lucerne and melilot may yet be seen at high elevations; both have been found beside the A66 at lower altitude.

Roadside verges that are covered by chemical sprays by local authorities have their plant life radically changed, losing such delightful species as bird's-eye primrose, cowslip and even common primrose. Wild orchids are not growing in the abundance of former years. The use of artificial manures on upland meadows has undoubtedly affected many glamorous flowers. Orchids cannot tolerate these manures. Aerial spraying to eradicate bracken has been practised on parts of the Pennines. What effects does this practice have on other plants? We do not really know.

As mentioned in an earlier chapter, many changes in the vegetation came about long before man came on the scene. Changes still happen, but now the effects of man's activities combine with natural influences to alter the vegetation.

The areas in the Pennines least affected by man are of great importance for understanding these changes, and in order to conserve such areas for studying how nature alone affects them, access is strictly limited to bona fide research workers. Moorhouse Nature Reserve and parts of Upper Teesdale are two examples.

Often a nature reserve has to be carefully managed to maintain a particularly good habitat which, if left to nature, might become overgrown and obliterated. For example, limestone pavements and pasture with their attractive flora would become covered by woodland if sheep were not there to graze down seedlings.

National Nature Reserves, reserves managed by county Naturalists' Trusts or other bodies, and privately owned reserves, are each under special care for particular reasons. Many other areas that are good for flowers are on private land. It is essential, therefore, that permission be sought to visit these places from the appropriate owner.

However, there are many areas open to the public and accessible by the vast network of footpaths in the Pennines where most of the flowers in our list may be found and enjoyed. Moreover, books and booklets describing Pennine walks are readily available, while guides to nature trails are a useful source of information. The new Ordnance Survey 1:25,000 Outdoor Leisure Maps showing the definitive footpaths give yet another way of planning where to go. The National Park Visitor Centres give a lot of help.

Whether in places of public access or on private land with permission, the same principles of care for the countryside and avoidance of habitat destruction apply. Hazards for the walker must also be remembered, especially on boggy or other unstable ground, and in places where old mine shafts and their ventilation chimneys might be hidden by vegetation.

The length of the chosen walk is of some significance. One could hardly expect a walker of the Three Peaks to return with a long plant list, yet he might have spotted some of the rarer species of high altitudes and noticed places to investigate on a more leisurely occasion. A long walk has the advantage of giving a picture of the whole countryside and its vegetation in relation to geology. Normally the botanist's pace is quite slow, for it does take time to look at and list all the flowers, but this is the most enjoyable way as long as one's companions are of like mind. Recording of species could produce information which would be useful and necessary for assessing future vegetational changes.

The list of walks given below is a selection from the many available, chosen to give examples of a variety of habitats and places.

Throughout this book we have purposely not indicated localities for the different species. Rather we would wish the reader to go out into the Pennines with some basic knowledge, a map or guide booklet, a useful flower book, notebook, pencil and lens, and an inquiring mind. There is then every chance of really finding out for oneself and making discoveries, the joy of which will never be forgotten.

The Northern Pennines

Cross Fell

Botanising is not likely to be the reason for anyone but the specialist to visit the summit plateau of Cross Fell, at 2,930 feet the highest point on the Pennines. It is prime walking country being on the route of the Pennine Way. A branch of this footpath leads directly over the summit. Cairns protrude from the *Rhacomitrium*, lichen, sedge and coarse grass to give the fell top an inhospitable appearance. For much of the time, Cross Fell is blotted out by cloud or mist. Snow cover varies from year to year, but averages 70 days a year. Drifts have been visible from Penrith on Midsummer Day. The Helm Wind is at home around Cross Fell. Temperatures below freezing have been recorded at Moor House on average for 132 days of the year, while rainfall occurred on average on 250 days. Incidentally, the Moor House Reserve is about four miles from Cross Fell top and 1,000 feet lower.

Despite the inhospitable climate, a few places not far from the summit of Cross Fell are worth searching for plants. It is a thrill to find a British plant that has not been recorded at such high altitude before. The interesting paper by Albert Wilson on *The Altitudinal Range of British Plants* (North-western Naturalist Vol. III, 1949) gives the criteria for a study of this kind.

High Cup Nick

To many, this enormous gash is the most spectacular feature on the Pennines. Here are dolerite columns of the whin-sill, eroded in some cases to the point of collapse. Debris and scree now cover about 20 per cent. of the steep slopes extending to the stream more than 600 ft. below. This stream eventually becomes the Trout Beck and joins the Eden at Kirkby Thore. Within a few yards of the source, small runners feed the Maize Beck and this watercourse flows into the Tees on the eastern side of the watershed.

Plants recorded at High Cup Nick early this century include *Potentilla sibbaldi*. This species does not seem to occur now, nor is alpine saxifrage now reported. Several flowers known as common a few decades ago and now scarce include meadow rue and alpine pennycress. In *The Flora of Westmorland*, Wilson (1938) briefly mentions New Zealand willowherb as occurring at Grasmere and Kendal. Now it is widespread at many montane sites, and particularly so in High Cup Nick.

Looking for plants on rocky insecure sites can be both arduous and hazardous. On account of the insecure holds, and the free-splitting of the rock, great care must be taken. The flora of High Cup bears more affinity to that of the Lakeland Fells than to the rest of the Pennines. Parsley fern occurs in the Nick, and else-where on the Pennines it is rare. Rose-root is abundant in High Cup, and also in the nearby Maize Beck gorge, which is an exciting place, being a small canyon of limestone. Alpine cinque-foil is the most attractive plant, but northern bedstraw is also showy. Butterwort can form an attractive display; its leafy rosettes and fine purple spurred flowers are closely spaced along the terraces of the cliffs. Small scabious blooms well. Alpine bistort can be encountered in the no-man's land between the Nick and the gorge.

Grass of Parnassus is to be seen in the lower part of the valley, at c. 1,100 feet, and with it grow devils-bit scabious and red rattle. The great woodrush can look very effective at places where it grows on a ledge along with early purple orchid and rose-root.

The minute flower of water blinks has to be searched for in wet places along the Pennine Way. The mountain pansy can appear along the sides of the footpath where the grass is short, and dog violet represents this family earlier in the spring. Lady's smock is also common. *Primula farinosa*, by which the mealy or bird's-eye primrose may be best-known, grows in the district. Alpine scurvy grass is to be found along the waterfalls and wet rocks of the Nick. At times its flowers seem to illuminate the area. Wood-sorrel attains a high altitude.

Widdybank Fell

A favourite walk in Upper Teesdale is the route of the Widdy-bank Fell Nature Trail, which goes along the track beside Cow Green Reservoir, linking up to the Pennine Way at Cauldron Snout. Reference has already been made to the flora of this area in the Upper Teesdale National Nature Reserve. An illustrated booklet produced by the Nature Conservancy Council may be obtained from the dispenser near the car park at the start of the trail. With the aid of this guide, the visitor can learn about the ecology of this unique habitat. If the flowers are to be there for future generations to enjoy, it is essential to avoid trampling and keep to the track from which all the plants may be seen.

Moor House National Nature Reserve

A special permit would be needed to go on to this reserve, which lies to the north of High Cup Nick. There is, however, a Pennine Moorland Nature Trail at the site, with a guide written by the Nature Conservancy Council and obtainable from the Officer-in-Charge at Moor House.

Upper Weardale

The walks mentioned so far are in the high Pennines. The Pennine Dales must be included among places to visit. A good example in the northern region is given by the walk in Hamsterley Forest, Upper Weardale, the route being described in the AA Book of Country Walks and the area classed as "mixed woodland on the fringe of the Pennines." A good deal of afforestation has taken place on both sides of the Bedburn Beck, and the first part of the walk follows the Forestry Commission's nature trail, for which an information leaflet is available. Botanists will find special interest in noting the difference in the flora seen on reaching Pikeston Fell where there are the remains of lead mines and quarries.

Central Pennines

We include just a few of the many walks in this very popular area, across which passes the Dales Way.

Upper Wharfedale

Near the Dales Way at Buckden is a good walk to Buckden Pike, and one of the guides to the route may be found in *Walking in the Craven Dales.* There is a Yorkshire Dales National Park Information board at Buckden and the Park authorities have provided an unobtrusive car park and picnic area. The limestone pastures and rocky outcrops make for exciting flower study on this lovely fell side above the Wharfe valley. It gives an opportunity to learn some of the different white-flowered species mentioned in the chapter on identification. A careful search among the rocks will reveal tiny flowering plants and ferns typical of this habitat. It would not be surprising if the walker, so absorbed in botany, failed to reach the summit of the Pike. A walk of shorter distance over the fell is still very rewarding.

Ingleton Glens

At Ingleton, on the west side of the Pennines, the well-known popular walk round the falls with their majestic beauty and great geological interest also provides for the botanist an excellent wild flower walk. Several of the guides to walks listed below include this excursion.

Malham Tarn Estate

Malham is another famous area notable for its scenic beauty, geology and flora. The estate is a nature reserve owned by the National Trust and managed by the Field Studies Council, which runs the Malham Tarn Field Centre. The Pennine Way passes through the estate, and it was here in April 1965 that the completion of the Way was celebrated; one of the authors was present on this historic occasion when a gathering of over 2,000 attended. The visitor who is not walking a long distance may travel slowly and enjoy the flowers on a part of the Way where a nature trail has been laid out by the centre staff. There is a booklet about the trail, giving helpful information and explaining some of the complex geology of the Malham area.

Bolton Abbey Woods

A section of the Dales Way at Bolton Abbey in Wharfedale through the woods and by the Strid gives a good example of a wooded valley in the Pennine Dales. There is a footpath on either side of the river. The land is privately owned, being part of the Chatsworth Estates, but public access is allowed. On the west bank, a small charge is made for the Strid Wood Nature Trails, where five trails—named and marked by their colours— have been organised. An attractive illustrated guide may be bought at the start. Perhaps the best time to go to Strid Wood is in spring when the trees are coming into leaf, birds are singing and the early woodland plants are in flower. But at all seasons the woods are a delight. In this area the limestone is not very far below the surface millstone grit and the botanical evidence of more basic places is the appearance of certain plants commoner in limestone districts. It is interesting that Bolton Abbey Woods have been famous for their flowers for many years and were often quoted as the locality for particular species in the old Floras. The Estate aims to conserve the woods and appreciates the co-operation of visitors so that people in the future may enjoy them as much as past and present generations.

Ilkley Moor

This famous Moor is the subject of a continuing ecological survey started by the Wharfedale Naturalists' Society in 1959. The study has been a means of assessing changes in the vegetation of the Moor since the turn of the century and these have proved very interesting. For the visitor there is the chance to learn the species of plants typical of a gritstone moor and to follow the nature trail mapped out by the Society. The members have produced a guide booklet to the trail based on the survey results and copies may be bought at the Tourist Information Centre, Ilkley Public Library (personal applications only). As well as the typical flowering plants and ferns of an acid moor, there are species that grow in less acid conditions and occur in places where there is some lime source such as a spring or lime-stone remnant in a glacial moraine. In addition, many common species of waste places grow within the boundary of the Moor and incidentally the New Zealand willowherb has made its home in one of the gills.

Southern Pennines

Moors of the Brontë Country

For botanising on wilder moorland several good walks are to be recommended around Haworth and some of the routes link up with the Pennine Way which then continues south passing near to Hebden Bridge.

Hardcastle Crags

This area in the Hebden Valley, owned by the National Trust, is a deep wooded clough with Hebden Water running through. The Halifax Scientific Society has been studying Hardcastle Crags for many years and noting the changes and status of species. To commemorate the Society's Centenary in 1974, members published a booklet on *Nature in Hardcastle Crags*. An appended list of flowering plants and ferns gives 270 species found in the Hebden Valley. The Society is rightly concerned that this "lovely valley" should be conserved.

Edale

At the southern extremity of the upland area selected for this book is Edale, the start of the Pennine Way for those travelling north. The Peak Park Planning Board has designated this first section of the Way as the Edale Nature Trail and has published an illustrated guide obtainable at the Information Centre. The route is via Grindsbrook to the plateau on Edale Moor, returning over Grindslow Knoll. Those following the trail will find the booklet especially helpful in explaining the nature of the soil, rock layers and peat, as well as woodland and moorland flora.

The northern arc of the Peakland Way covers the wild upland country of this area. It is a strenuous walk, starting from Barber Booth and following the eastern alternative route of the Pennine Way via Kinder Low, Kinder Downfall and Snake Pass to Hagg Farm. The botanist could select accessible sections but must always be aware of and prepared for adverse weather conditions. This advice applies whenever a walk in the Pennines is taken, especially at high altitude, and to the botanical necessities carried must be added the standard equipment for walkers.

Guides to Pennine Walks

The Pennine Way   Tom Stephenson   H.M.S.O.
The Pennine Way   Kenneth Oldham   Dalesman.
Walks on the Pennine Way   Colourmaster Publication.
The Dales Way   Colin Speakman   Dalesman.
Walks in Limestone Country   A. Wainwright
                                      Westmorland Gazette.
Walking in the Northern Dales   Ramblers' Association
                                      Dalesman.
Walking in the Craven Dales   Colin Speakman   Dalesman.
Walking in Airedale   Ramblers' Association   Dalesman.
*Walks for Motorists in the Yorkshire Dales; Further Dales Walks
    for Motorists,* and *Pendleside and Brontë Country Walks for
    Motorists*   Ramblers' Association   Gerrard Publications.
Haworth and the Brontës   W. R. Mitchell   Dalesman.
South Pennine Park   Herbert C. Collins   Dalesman.
Pennine Walks around Hebden Bridge   Calder Civic Trust.
The Peakland Way   John N. Merrill   Dalesman.
No Through Road   The AA Book of Country Walks.

The English Tourist Board and the British Tourist Authority
   publish information about nature trails.

*   *   *

Dales Rail trains, organised by the Yorkshire Dales National
Park Committee, in conjunction with British Rail, operate on
the Settle Carlisle line, monthly at weekends during the season.
From stations en route the visitor may take a walk in the
Pennines and return by train the same day. Full details
from Yorkshire Dales National Park Office, Yorebridge House,
Bainbridge, Leyburn, North Yorkshire.

STONE BRAMBLE

Check List of Selected Plants

Abbreviations

Where a species is known to be confined to or have preference for a particular soil this is indicated:

a=acid; n=neutral; b=basic.

Ref.: *Flora of the British Isles,* Clapham, Tutin and Warburg.

Distribution:

W=common and widespread species distributed over whole area. Other species distributed in suitable habitats:

P throughout area.

N in northern section.

M in central section.

S in southern section.

Ref.: *Atlas of the British Flora,* ed. F. H. Perring and S. M. Walters.

spp. =species (plural).

agg. =aggregate species, the name including one or more closely related species or subspecies.

Clubmosses, horsetails and ferns

Fir Clubmoss	*Lycopodium selago*		P
Stag's-horn Clubmoss	*L. clavatum*		P
Lesser Clubmoss	*Selaginella selaginoides*		NM
Water Horsetail	*Equisetum fluviatile*		P
Marsh Horsetail	*E. palustre*		P
Wood Horsetail	*E. sylvaticum*	a	P
Field Horsetail	*E. arvense*		W
Great Horsetail	*E. telmateia*		P
Bracken	*Pteridium aquilinum*	a	W
Parsley Fern	*Cryptogramma crispa*	a	NM
Hard Fern	*Blechnum spicant*	a	P
Hart's-tongue Fern	*Phyllitis scolopendrium*		P
Maidenhair Spleenwort	*Asplenium trichomanes*	b	P
Green Spleenwort	*A. viride*	b	NM

82

Wall-rue	*A. ruta-muraria*	b	P
Rustyback	*Ceterach officinarum*	b	NM
Lady-fern	*Athyrium filix-femina*	a	P
Brittle Bladder-fern	*Cystopteris fragilis*	b	NM
Male-fern	*Dryopteris filix-mas*		W
Scaly Male-fern	*D. pseudomas* (*D. borreri*)	a	P
Broad Buckler-fern	*D. dilatata*		P
Hard Shield-fern	*Polystichum aculeatum*		P
Lemon-scented Fern	*Thelypteris limbosperma*		P
	(*T. oreopteris*)	a	
Beech Fern	*T. phegopteris*	a	P
Oak Fern	*Gymnocarpium dryopteris*	a	P
Limestone Fern	*G. robertianum*	b	NM
Polypody	*Polypodium vulgare*		P
Moonwort	*Botrychium lunaria*		P
Adder's-tongue	*Ophioglossum vulgatum*		P

Conifers

Larch	*Larix decidua*	introduced	P
Scots Pine	*Pinus sylvestris*	introduced	P
Juniper	*Juniperus communis*	b	NM
Yew	*Taxus baccata*	b	NM

Flowering Plants—Dicotyledons
Ranunculaceae

Marsh Marigold	*Caltha palustris*		W
Globeflower	*Trollius europaeus*		NM
Baneberry	*Actaea spicata*	b	M
Wood Anemone	*Anemone nemorosa*		W
Meadow Buttercup	*Ranunculus acris*		W
Creeping Buttercup	*R. repens*		W
Bulbous Buttercup	*R. bulbosus*		P
Goldilocks	*R. auricomus*		P
Lesser Spearwort	*R. flammula*		W
Ivy-leaved Crowfoot	*R. hederaceus*		P
Round-leaved Crowfoot	*R. omiophyllus*		P
	(*R. lenormandi*)	a, n	P
Water Crowfoots			P
Lesser Celandine	*R. ficaria*		W
Columbine	*Aquilegia vulgaris*	b	NM
Lesser Meadow-rue	*Thalictrum minus*	b	NM

Papaveraceae

Welsh Poppy	*Meconopsis cambrica* introduced		NM

Cruciferae

Alpine Penny-cress	*Thlaspi alpestre*	b	NM
Shepherd's Purse	*Capsella bursa-pastoris*		W
Alpine Scurvy-grass	*Cochlearia alpina*		NM

Species		
Hoary Whitlowgrass *Draba incana*	b	NM
Wall Whitlowgrass *D. muralis*	b	NM
Spring Whitlowgrass *Erophila verna*		P
Cuckooflower *Cardamine pratensis* (Lady's Smock)		W
Large Bitter-cress *C. amara*		P
Wavy Bitter-cress *C. flexuosa*		P
Hairy Bitter-cress *C. hirsuta*		P
Winter-cress *Barbarea vulgaris*		P
Hairy Rockcress *Arabis hirsuta*	b	NM
Water-cress *Rorippa* spp.		P
Garlic Mustard *Alliaria petiolata* (Jack-by-the-hedge)		P
Thale Cress *Arabidopsis thaliana*		P

Violaceae

Hairy Violet *Viola hirta*	b	M
Common Dog-violet *V. riviniana*		W
Early Dog-violet *V. reichenbachiana*	b	P
Marsh Violet *V. palustris*		P
Mountain Pansy *V. lutea*		NM

Polygalaceae

Common Milkwort *Polygala vulgaris*		P
Heath Milkwort *P. serpyllifolia*		P

Guttiferae

Common St. John's-wort *Hypericum perforatum*	b	P
Square-stalked St. John's-wort *H. tetrapterum*		P
Trailing St. John's-wort *H. humifusum*	a, n	P
Slender St. John's-wort *H. pulchrum*		P
Hairy St. John's-wort *H. hirsutum*	b	P

Cistaceae

Common Rock-rose *Helianthemum chamaecistus*	b	NM

Caryophyllaceae

Red Campion *Silene dioica*		W
Ragged Robin *Lychnis flos-cuculi*		W
Common Mouse-ear *Cerastium holosteoides*		W
Sticky Mouse-ear *C. glomeratum*		P
Wood Stitchwort *Stellaria nemorum*		P
Common Chickweed *S. media*		W
Greater Stitchwort *S. holostea*		W
Lesser Stitchwort *S. graminea*		P
Bog Stitchwort *S. alsine*		P
Annual Pearlwort *Sagina apetala*		P
Procumbent Pearlwort *S. procumbens*		W
Knotted Pearlwort *S. nodosa*		NM
Spring Sandwort *Minuartia verna* (Leadwort)	b	NM
Three-nerved Sandwort *Moehringia trinervia*		P
Thyme-leaved Sandwort *Arenaria serpyllifolia*		P

Portulaceae

Blinks *Montia fontana*	a, n	P

Chenopodiaeceae
Good-King-Henry   *Chenopodium bonus-henricus*   P
Fat-hen   *C. album*   P
Common Orache   *Atriplex patula*   P

Linaceae
Fairy Flax   *Linum catharticum*   P

Geraniaceae
Meadow Crane's-bill   *Geranium pratense*   P
Wood Crane's-bill   *G. sylvaticum*   NM
Bloody Crane's-bill   *G. sanguineum*   b   M
Cut-leaved Crane's-bill   *G. dissectum*   P
Dove's-foot Crane's-bill   *G. molle*   P
Shining Crane's-bill   *G. lucidum*   b   NM
Herb-Robert   *G. robertianum*   W

Oxalidaceae
Wood Sorrel   *Oxalis acetosella*   W

Balsaminaceae
Indian Balsam   *Impatiens glandulifera* (Policeman's Helmet)
                                            introduced   P

Aceraceae
Sycamore   *Acer pseudoplatanus*   introduced   W
Field Maple   *A. campestris*   P

Hippocastaniaceae
Horse Chestnut   *Aesculus hippocastanum* introduced   P

Aquifoliaceae
Holly   *Ilex aquifolium*   W

Celastraceae
Spindle   *Euonymus europaeus*   b   M

Rhamnaceae
Buckthorn   *Rhamnus catharticus*   b   M

Papilionaceae or Leguminosae
Dyer's Greenweed   *Genista tinctoria*   P
Petty Whin   *G. anglica* (Needle Furze)   P
Gorse   *Ulex europaeus*   a, n   W
Western Gorse   *U. gallii*   a   MS
Medick   *Medicago lupulina*   P
Red Clover   *Trifolium pratense*   W
Zigzag Clover   *T. medium*   P
White Clover   *T. repens*   W
Lesser Trefoil   *T. dubium*   P
Kidney Vetch   *Anthyllis vulneraria*   b   P
Common Bird's-foot-trefoil   *Lotus corniculatus*   W
Greater Bird's-foot-trefoil   *L. uliginosus*   P
Horseshoe Vetch   *Hippocrepis comosa*   b   M
Tufted Vetch   *Vicia cracca*   P
Bush Vetch   *V. sepium*   W
Meadow Vetchling   *Lathyrus pratensis*   W

85

Bitter Vetch   *L. montanus*   P
Rosaceae
Dropwort   *Filipendula vulgaris*   b   mainly M
Meadowsweet   *F. ulmaria*   W
Cloudberry   *Rubus chamaemorus*   P
Stone Bramble   *R. saxatilis*   b   NM
Raspberry   *R. idaeus*   W
Bramble   *R. fruticosus* agg.   W
Shrubby Cinquefoil   *Potentilla fruticosa*   b   N
Marsh Cinquefoil   *P. palustris*   P
Barren Strawberry   *P. sterilis*   W
Silverweed   *P. anserina*   W
Spring Cinquefoil   *P. tabernaemontani*   b   M
Alpine Cinquefoil   *P. crantzii*   b   NM
Tormentil   *P. erecta*   mainly a   W
Trailing Tormentil   *P. anglica*   MS
Creeping Cinquefoil   *P. reptans*   b, n   W
Wild Strawberry   *Fragaria vesca*   mainly b   P
Wood Avens   *Geum urbanum*   W
Water Avens   *G. rivale*   W
Mountain Avens   *Dryas octopetala*   b   NM
Lady's-mantle   *Alchemilla vulgaris* agg.   W
Great Burnet   *Sanguisorba officinalis*   P
Salad Burnet   *Poterium sanguisorba*   b   P
Field Rose   *Rosa arvensis*   mainly S
Burnet Rose   *R. pimpinellifolia*   NM
Dog Rose   *R. canina*   P
Downy Rose   *R. villosa*   P
Blackthorn   *Prunus spinosa* (Sloe)   W
Bird Cherry   *P. padus*   P
Hawthorn   *Crataegus monogyna*   W
Rowan   *Sorbus aucuparia*   W
Crassulaceae
Roseroot   *Sedum rosea*   NM
Orpine   *S. telephium*   NM
Biting Stonecrop   *S. acre*   b   P
Hairy Stonecrop   *S. villosum*   NM
Saxifragaceae
Starry Saxifrage   *Saxifraga stellaris*   N
Rue-leaved Saxifrage   *S. tridactylites*   b   NM
Meadow Saxifrage   *S. granulata*   b, n   P
Mossy Saxifrage   *S. hypnoides*   b   NM
Yellow Saxifrage   *S. azoides*   N
Purple Saxifrage   *S. oppositifolia*   b   M
Opposite-leaved Golden Saxifrage

                              Chrysosplenium oppositifolium   P
Alternate-leaved Golden Saxifrage   *C. alternifolium*   P

Parnassiaceae
Grass-of-Parnassus   *Parnassia palustris*   P
Grossulariaceae
Downy Currant   *Ribes spicatum*   b   NM
Mountain Currant   *R. alpinum*   b   M
Droseraceae
Round-leaved Sundew   *Drosera rotundifolia*   P
Onagraceae
Great Willowherb   *Epilobium hirsutum* (Codlins and Cream) P
Hoary Willowherb   *E. parviflorum*   P
Broad-leaved Willowherb   *E. montanum*   W
Short-fruited Willowherb   *E. obscurum*   P
Marsh Willowherb   *E. palustre*   a   P
Alpine Willowherb   *E. anagallidifolium*   N
Chickweed Willowherb   *E. alsinifolium*   N
New Zealand Willowherb   *E. nerterioides* introduced   P
Rosebay Willowherb   *E. angustifolium*   W
Enchanter's-nightshade   *Circaea lutetiana*   P
Callitrichaceae
Common Water-starwort   *Callitriche stagnalis*   P
Araliaceae
Ivy   *Hedera helix*   W
Umbelliferae
Marsh Pennywort   *Hydrocotyle vulgaris*   a   P
Sanicle   *Sanicula europaea*   P
Cow Parsley   *Anthriscus sylvestris*   W
Sweet Cicely   *Myrrhis odorata*   P
Pignut   *Conopodium majus*   W
Burnet-saxifrage   *Pimpinella saxifraga*   b   P
Ground-elder   *Aegopodium podagraria* (Goutweed)
                                        ? introduced   W
Wild Angelica   *Angelica sylvestris*   W
Hogweed   *Heracleum sphondylium*   W
Euphorbiaceae
Dog's Mercury   *Mercurialis perennis*   W
Polygonaceae
Knotgrass   *Polygonum aviculare*   W
Alpine Bistort   *P. viviparum*   NM
Common Bistort   *P. bistorta*   a, n   P
Redshank   *P. persicaria*   W
Sheep's Sorrel   *Rumex acetosella*   a   W
Common Sorrel   *R. acetosa*   W
Northern Dock   *R. longifolius* (Butter Dock)   NM
Curled Dock   *R. crispus*   W
Broad-leaved Dock   *R. obtusifolius*   W
Wood Dock   *R. sanguineus*   P
Urticaceae

Species		Code
Common Nettle *Urtica dioica*		W
Ulmaceae		
Wych Elm *Ulmus glabra*		W
Betulaceae		
Silver Birch *Betula pendula*		P
Downy Birch *B. pubescens*		P
Alder *Alnus glutinosa*		W
Corylaceae		
Hazel *Corylus avellana*		W
Fagaceae		
Beech *Fagus sylvatica* introduced in Pennines		W
Pedunculate Oak *Quercus robur*		P
Sessile Oak *Q. petraea*	mainly a	P
Salicaceae		
Aspen *Populus tremula*		P
Bay Willow *Salix pentandra*		P
Purple Willow *S. purpurea*		P
Osier *S. viminalis*		P
Goat Willow *S. caprea* (Sallow)		P
Eared Willow *S. aurita*	a or slightly b	P
Tea-leaved Willow *S. phylicifolia*		NM
Creeping Willow *S. repens*		P
Ericaceae		
Bog Rosemary *Andromeda polifolia*		P
Bearberry *Arctostaphylos uva-ursi*		N
Heather *Calluna vulgaris*	a	W
Cross-leaved Heath *Erica tetralix*		P
Bell Heather *E. cinerea*		P
Cowberry *Vaccinium vitis-idaea*	a	P
Bilberry *V. myrtillus*	a	W
Cranberry *V. oxycoccos*		P
Empetraceae		
Crowberry *Empetrum nigrum*	a	P
Plumbaginaceae		
Thrift *Armeria maritima*		NM
Primulaceae		
Bird's-eye Primrose *Primula farinosa*	b	NM
Cowslip *P. veris*	b	P
Primrose *P. vulgaris*		P
Yellow Pimpernel *Lysimachia nemorum*		P
Bog Pimpernel *Anagallis tenella*		P
Oleaceae		
Ash *Fraxinus excelsior*	mainly b and n	W
Wild Privet *Ligustrum vulgare*	b	P
Gentianaceae		
Spring Gentian *Gentiana verna*	b	N
Field Gentian *Gentianella campestris*	a, n	P

Autumn Gentian *G. amarella* (**Felwort**)	b	P
Menyanthaceae		
Bogbean *Menyanthes trifoliata*	b, n	P
Boraginaceae		
Water Forget-me-not *Myosotis scorpioides*		P
Creeping Forget-me-not *M. secunda*	a, n	P
Pale Forget-me-not *M. stolonifera* (*M. brevifolia*)		P
Tufted Forget-me-not *M. caespitosa*		P
Wood Forget-me-not *M. sylvatica*		NM
Field Forget-me-not *M. arvensis*		P
Scrophulariaceae		
Common Figwort *Scrophularia nodosa*		W
Water Figwort *S. auriculata* (*S. aquatica*)		P
Green Figwort *S. umbrosa*		M
Monkeyflower *Mimulus guttatus*		P
Foxglove *Digitalis purpurea*	a	P
Brooklime *Veronica beccabunga*		W
Heath Speedwell *V. officinalis*		W
Marsh Speedwell *V. scutellata*	a	P
Wood Speedwell *V. montana*		P
Germander Speedwell *V. chamaedrys* (**Bird's Eye**)		W
Thyme-leaved Speedwell *V. serpyllifolia*		P
Wall Speedwell *V. arvensis*		P
Ivy-leaved Speedwell *V. hederifolia*		P
Common Field-speedwell *V. persica* introduced		P
Slender Speedwell *V. filiformis* introduced	mainly	NM
Marsh Lousewort *Pedicularis palustris* (**Red Rattle**)		P
Lousewort *P. sylvatica*		P
Yellow Rattle *Rhinanthus minor*		P
Common Cow-wheat *Melampyrum pratense*		P
Eyebright *Euphrasia officinalis* agg.		P
Red Bartsia *Odontites verna*		P
Orobanchaceae		
Toothwort *Lathraea squamaria*		P
Lentibulariaceae		
Common Butterwort *Pinguicula vulgaris*		P
Labiatae		
Corn Mint *Mentha arvensis*		P
Water Mint *M. aquatica*		P
Marjoram *Origanum vulgare* usually	b	P
Wild Thyme *Thymus drucei*		NM
Wild Basil *Clinopodium vulgare*	b	NM
Selfheal *Prunella vulgaris*		W
Betony *Betonica officinalis*		P
Marsh Woundwort *Stachys palustris*		MS
Hedge Woundwort *S. sylvatica*		W
Yellow Archangel *Lamiastrum galeobdolon*		S

Red Deadnettle *Lamium purpureum*		P
White Deadnettle *L. album*		P
Ground-ivy *Glechoma hederacea*		P
Skullcap *Scutellaria galericulata*		S
Wood Sage *Teucrium scorodonia*	a, n	P
Bugle *Ajuga reptans*		P
Plantaginaceae		
Greater Plantain *Plantago major*		W
Hoary Plantain *P. media*	b, n	NM
Ribwort Plantain *P. lanceolata*		W
Sea Plantain *P. maritima*		NM
Campanulaceae		
Giant Bellflower *Campanula latifolia*		P
Harebell *C. rotundifolia*		W
Rubiaceae		
Crosswort *Cruciata laevipes* (*Galium cruciata*)		W
Woodruff *Galium odoratum* (*Asperula odorata*)	b	P
Northern Bedstraw *G. boreale*		NM
Hedge Bedstraw *G. mollugo*	usually b	P
Lady's Bedstraw *G. verum*		W
Heath Bedstraw *G. saxatile*	a	W
Limestone Bedstraw *G. sterneri*	b	NM
Common Marsh-bedstraw *G. palustre*		W
Fen Bedstraw *G. uliginosum*		P
Cleavers *G. aparine* (Goosegrass, Sticky Willie)		W
Caprifoliaceae		
Elder *Sambucus nigra*		W
Guelder-rose *Viburnum opulus*		P
Honeysuckle *Lonicera periclymenum*		P
Adoxaceae		
Moschatel *Adoxa moschatellina*		P
Valerianaceae		
Common Valerian *Valeriana officinalis*		P
Marsh Valerian *V. dioica*		P
Dipsacaceae		
Field Scabious *Knautia arvensis*		P
Small Scabious *Scabiosa columbaria*	b	NM
Devil's-bit Scabious *Succisa pratensis*		P
Compositae		
Common Ragwort *Senecio jacobaea*		P
Marsh Ragwort *S. aquaticus*		S
Groundsel *S. vulgaris*		W
Colt's-foot *Tussilago farfara*		W
Butterbur *Petasites hybridus*		P
Marsh Cudweed *Gnaphalium uliginosum*	a	P
Mountain Everlasting *Antennaria dioica*	b	NM
Goldenrod *Solidago virgaurea*		P

Daisy *Bellis perennis*		W
Hemp-agrimony *Eupatorium cannabinum*		MS
Yarrow *Achillea millifolium*		W
Sneezewort *A. ptarmica*		P
Pineappleweed *Matricaria matricarioides* introduced		W
Oxeye Daisy *Leucanthemum vulgare*		
(*Chrysanthemum leucanthemum*)		W
Feverfew *Tanacetum parthenium* (*C. parthenium*)		
probably introduced		P
Tansy *T. vulgare*		P
Carline Thistle *Carlina vulgaris*	b	P
Burdock *Arctium minus* agg.		W
Musk Thistle *Carduus nutans*	b	NM
Welted Thistle *C. acanthoides*		P
Spear Thistle *Cirsium vulgare*		W
Marsh Thistle *C. palustre*		W
Creeping Thistle *C. arvense*		W
Melancholy Thistle *C. heterophyllum*		P
Greater Knapweed *Centaurea scabiosa*	b	P
Common Knapweed *C. nigra*		W
Saw-wort *Serratula tinctoria*	b	NM
Nipplewort *Lapsana communis*		W
Cat's-ear *Hypochaeris radicata*		W
Autumn Hawkbit *Leontodon autumnalis*		W
Rough Hawkbit *L. hispidus*	b	P
Goat's-beard *Tragopogon pratensis* (Jack-go-to-bed-at-noon)		P
Wall Lettuce *Mycelis muralis* usually b		P
Smooth Sow-thistle *Sonchus oleraceus*		P
Prickly Sow-thistle *S. asper*		P
Hawkweeds *Hieracium* spp.		P
Mouse-ear Hawkweed *H. pilosella*		W
Smooth Hawk's-beard *Crepis capillaris*		P
Marsh Hawk's-beard *C. paludosa*		P
Dandelion *Taraxacum officinale*		W
Monocotyledons		
Hydrocharitaceae		
Canadian Waterweed *Elodea canadensis*		MS
Juncaginaceae		
Marsh Arrowgrass *Triglochin palustris*		P
Potamogetonaceae		
Broad-leaved Pondweed *Potamogeton natans*		P
Bog Pondweed *P. polygonifolius*	a	P
Red Pondweed *P. alpinus*	a, n	P
Curled Pondweed *P. crispus*		P
Opposite-leaved Pondweed *Groenlandia densa*		M
Liliaceae		
Bog Asphodel *Narthecium ossifragum*	a	P

Lily-of-the-valley *Convallaria majalis*	b	P
Bluebell *Endymion non-scriptus*		W
Field Garlic *Allium oleraceum*		P
Ramsons *A. ursinum* (Wild Garlic)		W
Trilliaceae		
Herb-Paris *Paris quadrifolia*	b	NM
Juncaceae		
Heath Rush *Juncus squarrosus*	a	W
Toad Rush *J. bufonius*		P
Hard Rush *J. inflexus*	b, n	P
Soft Rush *J. effusus*	a	W
Compact Rush *J. subuliflorus (J. conglomeratus)*	a	P
Sharp-flowered Rush *J. acutiflorus*	a	P
Jointed Rush *J. articulatus*	a	W
Bulbous Rush *J. bulbosus*	a	P
Hairy Wood-rush *Luzula pilosa*		P
Great Wood-rush *L. sylvatica*	a	P
Field Wood-rush *L. campestris*		W
Heath Wood-rush *L. multiflora*	a	P
Orchidaceae		
Broad-leaved Helleborine *Epipactis helleborine*		P
Common Twayblade *Listera ovata*	b	P
Lesser Twayblade *L. cordata*		P
Frog Orchid *Coeloglossum viride*	b	P
Fragrant Orchid *Gymnadenia conopsea*	b	P
Greater Butterfly-orchid *Platanthera chlorantha*	b	P
Lesser Butterfly-orchid *P. bifolia*	b	P
Fly Orchid *Ophrys insectifera*	b	M
Early-purple Orchid *Orchis mascula* mainly	b	P
Common Spotted-orchid *Dactylorhiza fuchsii*	b	P
Heath Spotted-orchid *D. maculata*	a	P
Northern Marsh-orchid *D. purpurella*	b	NM
Araceae		
Lords-and-Ladies *Arum maculatum*	b, n	P
Cyperaceae		
Common Cottongrass *Eriophorum angustifolium*	a	W
Hare's-tail Cottongrass *E. vaginatum*	a	W
Deergrass *Scirpus caespitosus*	a	P
Bristle Club-rush *S. setaceus*		P
Common Spike-rush *Eleocharis palustris*		P
Flat-sedge *Blysmus compressus*		NM
Tawny Sedge *Carex hostiana*	b	P
Green-ribbed Sedge *C. binervis*	a	P
Long-stalked Yellow-sedge *C. lepidocarpa*	b	NM
Common Yellow-sedge *C. demissa*	a	P
Wood-sedge *C. sylvatica*		P
Bottle Sedge *C. rostrata*		P

Common name	Scientific name		
Bladder-sedge	*C. vesicaria*		P
Lesser Pond-sedge	*C. acutiformis*	b	NM
Pale Sedge	*C. pallescens*		NM
Carnation Sedge	*C. panicea*		W
Glaucous Sedge	*C. flacca*	b	P
Hairy Sedge	*C. hirta*		P
Pill Sedge	*C. pilulifera*	b	P
Spring-sedge	*C. caryophyllea*	mainly a	P
Common Sedge	*C. nigra*		W
Brown Sedge	*C. disticha*		P
Star Sedge	*C. echinata*	a	W
Remote Sedge	*C. remota*		P
White Sedge	*C. curta*	a, n	P
Oval Sedge	*C. ovalis*		P
Flea Sedge	*C. pulicaris*	b	NM
Dioecious Sedge	*C. dioica*	b	NM
Gramineae			
Purple Moor-grass	*Molinia caerulea*	a	P
Heath-grass	*Sieglingia decumbens*		P
Floating Sweet-grass	*Glyceria fluitans*		P
Small Sweet-grass	*G. declinata*		P
Meadow Fescue	*Festuca pratensis*		P
Giant Fescue	*F. gigantea*		P
Red Fescue	*F. rubra*		P
Sheep's-fescue	*F. ovina*		W
Perennial Rye-grass	*Lolium perenne*		W
Annual Meadow-grass	*Poa annua*		W
Wood Meadow-grass	*P. nemoralis*		P
Smooth Meadow-grass	*P. pratensis*		W
Rough Meadow-grass	*P. trivialis*		P
Cock's-foot	*Dactylis glomerata*		W
Crested Dog's-tail	*Cynosurus cristatus*		W
Quaking-grass	*Briza media*		W
Wood Melick	*Melica uniflora*		P
Mountain Melick	*M. nutans*	b	NM
Blue Moor-grass	*Sesleria caerulea*	b	NM
Hairy-brome	*Bromus ramosus*		P
Soft-brome	*B. mollis*		P
False Brome	*Brachypodium sylvaticum*		P
Common Couch	*Agropyron repens*		P
Crested Hair-grass	*Koeleria cristata*	b	NM
Yellow Oat-grass	*Trisetum flavescens*	b, n	P
Meadow Oat-grass	*Helictotrichon pratense*	b	NM
Downy Oat-grass	*H. pubescens*	b	NM
False Oat-grass	*Arrhenatherum elatius*		W
Yorkshire-fog	*Holcus lanatus*		W
Creeping Soft-grass	*H. mollis*	moderately a	P

Tufted Hair-grass *Deschampsia caespitosa*			W
Wavy Hair-grass *D. flexuosa*	a		W
Early Hair-grass *Aira praecox*			P
Brown Bent *Agrostis canina*	a		P
Common Bent *A. tenuis*	mainly a		W
Creeping Bent *A. stolonifera*			P
Timothy *Phleum pratense*			W
Meadow Foxtail *Alopecurus pratensis*			P
Marsh Foxtail *A. geniculatus*			P
Sweet Vernal-grass *Anthoxanthum odoratum*			W
Reed Canary-grass *Phalaris arundinacea*			P
Mat-grass *Nardus stricta*	a, n		W

Books for Reference and Further Reading

1956 *Collins Pocket Guide to Wild Flowers.* David McClintock and R. S. R. Fitter.

1973 *Oxford Book of Wild Flowers.* B. E. Nicholson, S. Ary and M. Gregory.

1969 *The Concise British Flora in Colour.* W. Keeble Martin.

1975 *A Field Guide to Wild Flowers in Colour.* Dietmar Aichele.

1971 *The Scented Wild Flowers of Britain.* Roy Genders.

1974 *The Wild Flowers of Britain and Northern Europe.* Richard Fitter, Alastair Fitter and Marjorie Blamey.

1972 *Flowers of Europe.* Oleg Palunin.

1962 *Flora of the British Isles.* A. R. Clapham, T. G. Tutin and E. F. Warburg.

1973 *Excursion Flora of the British Isles.*

1945 *Wayside and Woodland Ferns.* Edward Step.

1974 *Ferns.* Roger Ground.

1968 *British Sedges.* A. C. Jermy and T. G. Tutin.

1968 *Grasses.* C. E. Hubbard.

1971 *Finding Wild Flowers.* R. S. R. Fitter.

1958 *List of British Vascular Plants.* J. E. Dandy.

1974 *English Names of Wild Flowers.* J. G. Dony, C. M. Rob and F. H. Perring.

1951 *A Key to the Names of British Plants.* R. D. Macleod.

1976 *Atlas of the British Flora.* Ed. F. H. Perring and S. M. Walters.

The Face of North-West Yorkshire. Arthur Raistrick and John L. Illingworth.

1968 *The Pennine Dales.* Arthur Raistrick.

1971 *The Naturalists' Yorkshire.* Yorkshire Naturalists' Union. Ed. W. A. Sledge.
1976 *The Natural History of Upper Teesdale.* Ed. M. E. Bradshaw.
1974 *History of British Vegetation.* Winifred Pennington.
1948 *The Pennines and Adjacent Areas.* D. A. Wray. Geological Survey, H.M.S.O.
1953 *Northern England.* T. Eastwood. Geological Survey, H.M.S.O.
1974 *The Peak District.* K. C. Edwards.
1950 *Mountains and Moorlands.* W. H. Pearsall.
1950 *Wild Flowers of the Chalk and Limestone.* J. E. Lousley.
1956 *Mountain Flowers.* John Raven and Max Walters.
1948 *British Plant Life.* W. B. Turrill.
1954 *Wild Flowers.* John Gilmour and Max Walters.
1961 *Weeds and Aliens.* Sir Edward Salisbury.
1973 *The Pollination of Flowers.* Michael Proctor and Peter Yeo.

Books related to Plant Lore

Culpeper's Complete Herbal.
Gerarde's Herbal, 1697.
The Herbal Encyclopedia (D. Lowe).
The Complete Book of Herbs (Sanecki).
Paradisus, John Parkinson, 1629.
A Modern Herbal, M. Grieve (New York, 1959).

GOOD KING HENRY

GRASS OF PARNASSUS

Finale

TO be at one of the attractive floral sites of the Pennines can give satisfaction and pleasure that well reward the efforts of getting there. Memories are created that linger a score of years or more.

Scenes coming to mind are the association of late primroses and early bluebells; bird's-eye primrose flowering in abundance along the shores of a high-level woodland pool; yellow mountain saxifrage blooming on the damp shoulder of a grassy hillside; Grass-of-Parnassus peeping through the rushes; cotton-grass waving in a breeze—all these have been worth more than a little effort to obtain such a view.

Change is always taking place in nature and the pace of change is accelerated by man's influence. We might not find all the flowers our forebears did, yet there are gains as well as losses and we may discover new arrivals. Some habitats will be lost for ever, but other changes of land usage may be only temporary and plants could recur when conditions are again suitable. The thrill of rediscovering a plant recorded in a place many years ago is always a possibility.

Whatever changes there may be in the flora of the Pennines, we believe that the words of Abraham Cowley, writing in the 17th century, will always ring true:

> *The trees as beauteous are and flowers as gay*
> *As ever they were wont to be.*